A LEVEL

Questions and Answers

BIOLOGY

Morton Jenkins

Examiner

Letts

EDUCATIONAL

SERIES EDITOR: BOB McDUELL

Contents

Introduction

HOW TO USE THIS BOOK

The aim of the *Questions and Answers* series is to provide students with the help required to attain the highest level of achievement in important examinations. This book is intended to help you with A- and AS-level Biology and Higher Level Biology in Scotland. The series relies on the premise that an experienced examiner can provide, through examination questions, sample answers and advice – the help a student needs to secure success. Many revision aids concentrate on providing factual information that might have to be recalled in an examination. This series, while giving factual information in an easy-to-remember form, concentrates on the other skills that need to be developed for the new A-level examinations to be held in 1996.

The Letts *Questions and Answers* series is designed to provide:

- Easy to use **Revision Summaries** which identify important factual information that the student must understand if progress is to be made in answering examination questions.

- Advice on the different types of question in each subject and how to answer them well to obtain the highest marks.

- Information about other skills that will be tested on examination papers apart from the recall of knowledge. These are sometimes called **Assessment Objectives**. Modern A-level examinations put great emphasis on the testing of other objectives apart from knowledge and understanding. Typically, questions testing these Assessment Objectives can make up 50% of the mark allocated to the written papers. Assessment Objectives include communication, problem solving, evaluation and interpretation. The *Questions and Answers* series is intended to develop these skills by the use of questions and the appreciation of outcomes by the student.

- Many examples of **examination questions**. Students can improve their performance by studying a sufficiently wide range of questions, providing they are shown the way to answer questions correctly. It is advisable that students try these questions before looking at the answers and the examiner's tips that follow them. The questions in this book are all specimen materials issued by Examination Boards and simulate the types of question to be expected in the examinations of 1996 and beyond.

- **Sample answers** to all of the questions.

- **Advice from the Examiner**. By using the experience of Chief Examiners we are able to give advice that can enable students to see how their answers can be improved and success be ensured.

Success in A-level examinations comes from proper preparation and a positive attitude to the examination, developed through a sound knowledge of facts and understanding of principles. The books are intended to overcome examination nerves which often develop from a fear of not being properly prepared.

THE IMPORTANCE OF USING QUESTIONS FOR REVISION

Past examination questions play an important part in revising for examinations. However, it is important not to start practising questions too early. Nothing can be more disheartening than trying to do a question which you do not understand because you have not mastered the topic. Therefore, it is important to have studied a topic thoroughly before attempting any questions on it.

How can past examination questions provide a way of preparing for the examination? It is unlikely that any question you try will appear in exactly the same form on the papers you are going to take. However, the examiner is restricted on what he can set since questions must cover the whole syllabus and test certain Assessment Objectives. The number of totally original questions you can set on any part of the syllabus is very limited and so similar ideas occur over and over again. It certainly will help you if the question you are trying to answer in an examination is familiar and you know you have done similar questions before. This is a great boost for your confidence and confidence is what is required for examination success.

Practising examination questions will also highlight gaps in your knowledge and understanding which you can go back and revise more thoroughly. It will also indicate which sorts of questions you can do well and which, if there is a choice of questions, you should avoid.

Attempting past questions will get you used to the type of language used in questions.

Finally, having access to answers, as you do in this book, will enable you to see clearly what is required by the examiner, how best to answer each question, and the amount of detail required. Attention to detail is a key aspect of achieving success at A level.

MAXIMISING YOUR MARKS

One of the keys to examination success is to know how marks are gained and lost by candidates. There are two important aspects to this: ensuring you follow the instructions (or 'rubric') on the examination paper and understanding how papers are marked by examiners.

Often candidates fail to gain the marks they deserve because they do not follow the rubric exactly. If you are asked to answer four questions from a section and you answer five, you can only receive credit for four. The examiner may be instructed to mark the first four only and cross out additional questions. It would be unfortunate if the fifth question was your best. Anyway, attempting too many questions means you will have wasted time. You cannot have spent the correct amount of time on each of the four questions and your answers could have suffered as a result.

Where a choice of questions is possible, candidates often choose the wrong questions. A question which looks familiar may not always be as easy as it seems and valuable time can be lost going up 'dead-ends'. If you have a choice, spend time before you start reading all of the questions and making rough notes. Then start with the questions you think you can do the best and leave any you are not sure about until later when, hopefully, your confidence will have grown. When choosing, look at the marks allocated to various parts of the questions and try to judge if you are confident in those parts where most marks are available.

For every examination paper there is a mark scheme, which tells the examiner where marks should and should not be awarded. For example, where a question is worth a maximum of five marks, there will be five, six or maybe more correct marking points and the examiner will award the first five given by the candidate. A '(5)' shown after a question on an exam paper is an indication that five points are required from your answer. Obviously, lengthy writing will not gain credit unless the candidate is hitting the right responses. Try therefore to keep your answers brief and to the point. Look at your answers critically after you have written them and try to decide how many different important points you have made.

An important principle of examination marking is called consequential marking. This means that if a candidate makes a mistake, the examiner must only penalise the candidate for it once. For example, if you made a mistake early in a calculation so that you came up with an incorrect value, you would obviously lose a mark. However, if you then used this incorrect value in a later part of the question, and your working was correct apart from this incorrect value, you would not lose any more marks. Therefore, always write down all of your workings, so that you can gain marks even if you make an early slip up. You will see examples of consequential marking in the questions in this book.

As a rough guide in an examination you should be aiming to score a mark each minute. When about 15 minutes of the examination remain, it is worth checking whether you are short of time. If you feel you are seriously running out of time, it is very important to try to score as many marks as possible in the short time that remains. In any question worth five marks, one or two will be easily scored and one or two will be very difficult to score. Concentrate on scoring the easy marks on each question that remains. Do not try to write sentences. Just put the main points down clearly in note form.

DIFFERENT TYPES OF EXAMINATION QUESTION

Structured questions

These are the most common type of question used in A-level Biology examinations. They can be short, with little opportunity for extended writing or they can be longer, with parts that demand lengthy answers of two or more paragraphs. They certainly will test higher-level skills of interpretation and evaluation.

Structured questions are divided into parts (a), (b), (c) etc., which may be subdivided into (i), (ii), (iii) etc. There are lines or spaces to answer each part and these can be a guide to the necessary detail and length of the expected answer. If you need more space to complete your answer then continue on a separate sheet of paper, which will be supplied in the examination. Make sure you label the separate sheet with your name, examination number, and the correct question e.g. 3(a)(iii).

A fair guide to timing yourself in an examination is an allocation of one minute per mark; i.e. if a question is worth 15 marks (this will be indicated at the end of the question), it should take about 15 minutes to answer.

It is most important to read and understand the **command** word in the question stem. The following glossary will help.

- **State** This means a brief answer is required with no supporting evidence. Alternatives include 'Write down'; 'Give'; 'List'; 'Name'.

- **Define** Only a concise and succinct definition is needed.

- **State and explain** A short answer is required, but then an explanation is needed. A question of this type will be worth more than one mark.

- **Describe** This is often used with reference to a particular experiment. The important points should be given about each stage and each point could be worth a mark.

- **Compare and contrast** In this type of question you need to look at similarities and differences. For example, 'Compare and contrast photosynthesis and respiration'. Before starting to answer this type of question, make a rough table with headings, similarities and differences.

- **Outline** The answer should be brief and the main points stated concisely.

- **Complete** You are required to add information to a diagram, sentence, flow chart, graph, identification key, table etc.

- **Calculate** A numerical answer is required. You should show your working in order to reach an answer. Use the correct units.
- **Suggest** There is not just one correct answer, or you are applying your answer to a situation outside the syllabus.

Free-response questions

These can include essays. In this type of question, you are given the opportunity to develop an answer in different ways. Your answer is strictly a free response and you may write as much as you wish. Candidates often do not write enough or, at the other extreme, they try to 'pad out' the answer.

Remember, you can only score marks when your answer matches the marking points on the examiner's mark scheme. It is important to plan your answer before starting it, allocating the correct amount of time to each important point.

Comprehension questions

Some Examination Boards set comprehension questions that may be compulsory. These questions often fill two or three pages. The answers to many of the questions that follow are given in the passage. Other answers can be deduced by understanding the passage. It is most important to read the passage thoroughly before attempting the questions. Read through the passage twice.

The first time you read it you should not refer to the questions. Try and understand the information you have been given. It may be unfamiliar Biology, but that does not matter because comprehension of given information is being tested. After reading the passage for a second time answer the questions that follow.

ASSESSMENT OBJECTIVES IN BIOLOGY

Assessment Objectives are the intellectual and practical skills you should be able to demonstrate. Opportunities must be made by the Examiner when setting the examination paper for you to demonstrate your mastery of these skills when you answer the question paper.

Traditionally, the Assessment Objective of knowledge and understanding has been regarded as the most important skill to develop. Candidates have been directed to learn large amounts of knowledge to recall in the examination.

Whilst not wanting in any way to devalue the learning of facts, it should be remembered that knowledge and understanding can only contribute about half of the marks on the written paper. The other half of the marks are acquired by mastery of the other Assessment Objectives. These are:

- Communicate scientific observations, ideas and arguements effectively.
- Select and use reference materials and translate data from one form to another.
- Interpret, evaluate and make informed judgements from relevant facts, observations and phenomena.
- Solve qualitative and quantitative problems.

1 Energy and life

The chemistry of life

❶ Elements cannot be simplified chemically. They consist of **atoms**, which, in turn, form combinations known as **molecules**. 99% of living matter is made of the elements carbon, hydrogen, oxygen, nitrogen, phosphorus and sulphur.

❷ An atom is made of a central **nucleus** containing **neutrons** and positively charged **protons**. The **atomic number** of an element is determined by the number of protons in the nucleus, and **isotopes** of elements exist because of variations in the number of neutrons. **Electrons** are negatively charged and orbit the nucleus in paths called **shells**. Each shell is at a specific distance from the nucleus and has a characteristic number of electrons in it. **Ions** are charged particles formed from the addition or loss of an electron to an atom.

❸ **Chemical reduction** results from a gain of an electron, whereas **oxidation** is the result of a loss of an electron or addition of oxygen.

❹ Atoms are held together by **bonds** when they form molecules. When electrons are transferred from one atom to another an **ionic bond** is formed due to the attractive forces between ions of opposite charge. When atoms share electrons, a **covalent bond** is formed. In some molecules, a shared electron is more strongly attracted to one of the atoms, polarizing the molecule. **Hydrogen bonds** are weak bonds in which the positive end of a polar molecule is attracted to the negative end of another polar molecule. Hydrogen bonding between water molecules gives water some of its unusual characteristics.

❺ All life is closely associated with carbon. It shares the four electrons in its outer shell when reacting with other atoms. Combinations of carbon and hydrogen are called **hydrocarbons**. Ring compounds or chains can be formed when carbon atoms join together.

❻ When molecules interact in chemical reactions bonds are either made or broken. **Energy of activation** is needed to initiate the reaction and this can be attained by heating the reactants, by increasing the concentration of the reactants, or by increasing pressure.

❼ The energy of activation can be lowered with the use of **catalysts**, thereby speeding up the **rate of reaction** without changing the nature or direction of the reaction. Biological catalysts are **proteins** called **enzymes**. The **substrate** on which the enzyme acts fits into the **active site** of the enzyme like a key fits into a lock. Enzymes are unchanged after they have worked on the substrate.

❽ Living organisms are made of molecules including **carbohydrates**, **lipids**, **proteins** and **nucleotides**. Carbohydrates are made of carbon, hydrogen and oxygen. Simple carbohydrates, called **monosaccharides**, are built into **disaccharides** or **polysaccharides** by removal of water (**condensation**). Large carbohydrates can be broken into their building blocks by addition of water in a process called **hydrolysis**. Animals store carbohydrates as **glycogen** by connecting many building blocks of glucose and monosaccharides **alpha linkages**. Plants form **cellulose** by connecting glucose units with different bonds, called **beta linkages**.

❾ Lipids are made of carbon, hydrogen and oxygen. They include **fats**, **waxes**, **phospholipids** and **steroids**. Fats are rich in energy and are made of **glycerol** and **fatty acids**. The carbon chains of **saturated** fats are filled with hydrogen atoms and are usually animal fats. Plant fats or **oils** are usually liquid at room temperature whereas animal fats are solid. Saturated fats have adverse effects on the cardiovascular system. Waxes are long chains of saturated fatty acids. Phospholipids are important parts of **cell membranes**. Steroids are lipids formed of four interlocking carbon rings with many side chains. **Cholesterol** and the sex hormones are examples of steroids.

❿ Proteins are long chains of nitrogen-containing **amino acids** linked by **peptide bonds**. Peptides, chains of up to 300 amino acid, can be joined to form proteins. About 20 types of amino acids are found in proteins. The sequence of amino acids forms the protein's **primary structure**. Hydrogen bonds between amino acids cause some proteins to form a stable, regular shape called its **secondary structure**. Some protein chains fold back on themselves, forming a clump. This folding is the **tertiary structure**. The **quaternary structure** is formed when two or more twisted protein chains combine.

⓫ Nucleotides are important in the formation of **RNA** and **DNA**. They contain a sugar, a phosphate group, and a nitrogen-containing **base**. The **pyrimidines** (thymine, cytosine, and uracil) have a single ring. The **purines** (adenine and guanine) have double rings.

Energy and living systems

❶ Energy is the ability to do work. **Potential** energy is stored energy that can be converted into other energy forms: **kinetic**, **electrical**, **mechanical**, **heat**, and **light**.

❷ The **laws of thermodynamics** govern the behaviour of all energy. The first law states that energy cannot be created or destroyed, but can change from one form into another. The second law states that when energy changes form, some will become unavailable to the system. As a result, processes move toward disorder (**entropy**). Therefore, living things must expend energy to remain organised.

❸ The sun's energy is stored in certain molecules by green plants, thereby becoming available to support all living systems.

❹ **ATP** (adenosine triphosphate) is the cell's energy currency. Energy is put into the molecule to add the third phosphate bond to **ADP**. When this bond is broken, the released energy can fuel processes taking place in the cell.

❺ **Photosynthesis** is the process by which plants use the sun's energy to make organic compounds. The sun's energy is captured by pigments such as the green pigments **chlorophyll a** and **b** and the orange pigment **carotene**. The overall result is that carbon dioxide and water are converted into glucose and oxygen.

❻ The **light-dependent** reactions of photosynthesis begin when light is captured by a pigment such as chlorophyll. Pigments are found in **chloroplasts**, which are double-membraned structures containing discs (**thylakoids**) and which are arranged in stacks called **grana**. The thylakoids from different grana are connected by membranous **lamellae**. Embedded in the thlakoid membrane are **CF-particles**, through which enzyme-laden channels connect the inside of the disc to the jelly-like **stroma** surrounding the thylakoids.

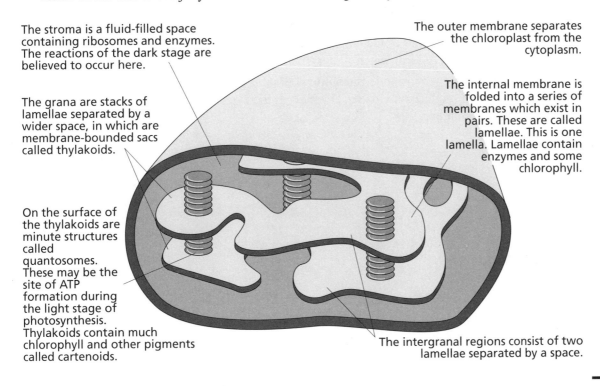

The stroma is a fluid-filled space containing ribosomes and enzymes. The reactions of the dark stage are believed to occur here.

The grana are stacks of lamellae separated by a wider space, in which are membrane-bounded sacs called thylakoids.

On the surface of the thylakoids are minute structures called quantosomes. These may be the site of ATP formation during the light stage of photosynthesis. Thylakoids contain much chlorophyll and other pigments called cartenoids.

The outer membrane separates the chloroplast from the cytoplasm.

The internal membrane is folded into a series of membranes which exist in pairs. These are called lamellae. This is one lamella. Lamellae contain enzymes and some chlorophyll.

The intergranal regions consist of two lamellae separated by a space.

❼ When light strikes a chlorophyll molecule in **photosystem II**, two of the chlorophyll's electrons move to a higher energy state where they can be captured by an electron acceptor and passed along an **electron transport chain** to another chlorophyll pigment system, **photosystem I**. After passing along a second transport chain, the electrons are used to reduce **NADP** to **NADPH**. The electrons taken from the chlorophyll in photosystem I are replaced by electrons from photosystem II and those, in turn, are replaced by electrons taken from water, so forming oxygen.

❽ Protons become more concentrated within the thylakoid because they are left there when the electrons are removed and passed along photosytem II, and because they are pumped in from the stroma. The proton accumulation within the thylakoid sets up a chemical and electrical gradient. In response to these gradients, protons move through the channels in the CF-particles. As they do so, the energy of their movement is used to produce ATP from ADP. This process is called **chemiosmosis**.

❾ The ATP and NADPH formed in the light-dependent reactions are used to form nutrient molecules in the **light-independent** reactions. The main biochemical pathway of the light-independent reactions is the **Calvin cycle**. The basic events are the addition of carbon dioxide to a five-carbon sugar, **ribulose bisphosphate** (RuBP), to form a six-carbon sugar that quickly splits into 2 three-carbon molecules of **phosphoglyceraldehyde** (**PGAL**), which can be converted to glucose, starch, or RuBP.

❿ During **respiration**, cells slowly release the energy in high-energy molecules and store it in ATP. The first step in this process, **glycolysis**, takes place in the cytoplasm and does not require oxygen. As each glucose molecule is converted into two molecules of pyruvate, there is a net gain of 2ATP, 2NADH and 2H. If oxygen is absent, pyruvate enters a pathway called **fermentation**, which produces ethanol plus carbon dioxide in yeast, and produces lactic acid in animal cells and some bacteria. In the presence of oxygen, the three-carbon pyruvate may be converted to two-carbon acetate, then combined with coenzyme A before it enters the **Krebs cycle**.

⓫ In the Krebs cycle, the energy in each of the two pyruvates from a glucose molecule is used to reduce three molecules of **NAD** to **NADH**, reduce one molecule of **FAD** to **FADH** and to form one molecule of ATP. Carbon dioxide is also produced.

⓬ In the electron transport chain, electrons that had been accepted by NAD and FAD are passed along a series of electron accptors, each at a lower energy level than the one before, releasing energy gradually. At the end of the chain, electrons join with protons to form hydrogen and then join with oxygen to form water.

⓭ ATP is produced by chemiosmotic **phosphorylation** as protons pass out of the **mitochondrion** through enzyme-laden channels in the **F-particles** embedded in the mitochondrial membrane.

If you need to revise this subject more thoroughly, see the relevant topics in the *Letts* A level *Biology Study Guide.*

1

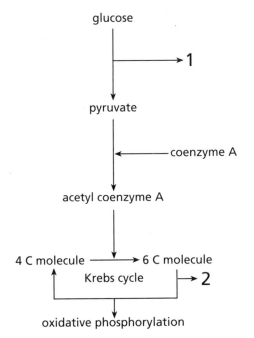

The diagram shows some of the processes in aerobic respiration.

(a) What TWO useful substances are produced during the stage labelled 1 on the diagram?

1 ....

2 ....   (2)

(b) What substance, containing 1 carbon atom, is released at the stage labelled 2 on the diagram?

....   (1)

(c) Explain briefly what happens during 'oxidative phosphorylation'.

....

....

....

....

....

.... (3)

NEAB

2 An investigation was carried out into the effect of carbon dioxide concentration and light intensity on the productivity of lettuces in a glasshouse. The productivity was determined by measuring the rate of carbon dioxide fixation in milligrams per dm^2 leaf area per hour.

Experiments were carried out at three different light intensities, 0.05, 0.25 and 0.45 (arbitrary units), the highest approximating to full sunlight. A constant temperature of 22°C was maintained throughout.

The results are given in the table below.

Carbon dioxide concentration /ppm	Productivity at different light intensities / mg dm^{-2} h^{-1}		
	At 0.05 units light intensity	At 0.25 units light intensity	At 0.45 units light intensity
300	12	25	27
500	14	30	36
700	15	36	42
900	15	37	46
1100	15	37	47
1300	12	31	46

(a) For the experiment at 0.25 units light intensity, describe and comment on the effect on the productivity of the lettuces of increasing carbon dioxide concentration in the ranges (i) 300 to 900 ppm, and (ii) 900 to 1300 ppm.

(i) 300 to 900 ppm

....

....

....

.... (2)

(ii) 900 to 1300 ppm

....

....

....

.... (2)

(b) (i) A carbon dioxide concentration of 300 ppm is approximately equivalent to that in atmospheric air.

For each of the three light intensities, work out the maximum increase in productivity that was obtained compared with that at 300 ppm and use it to calculate the percentage increase in productivity at each light intensity.

1   At 0.05 units light intensity

Maximum increase ....

Percentage increase ....

2   At 0.25 units light intensity

Maximum increase ....

Percentage increase ....

3   At 0.45 units light intensity

Maximum increase ....

Percentage increase.. (3)

(ii) Comment on the effect on productivity of changing light intensity.

....

....

....

.... (2)

(c) Explain why the carbon dioxide concentration affects the productivity of plants.

....

....

....

....

....

.... (3)

(d) State why the temperature should be kept constant during this experiment.

....

.... (1)

(e) Suggest why, even with artificial lighting, glasshouse crops generally need to have more carbon dioxide added when temperatures are low, than when temperatures are high.

....

....

....

.... (2)

ULEAC

3 The important pigments in most chloroplasts are the yellow-green chlorophyll *a*, the blue-green chlorophyll *b* and the orange carotenoids (mainly carotene). The diagram opposite shows (left *y*-axis) the *absorption spectra* of these pigments.

(a) Using the information shown, state concisely one piece of evidence which suggests that absorption of white light by chloroplasts is not uniform over the whole spectrum.

....

.... (1)

(b) Which colour of light is best absorbed by the carotenoids?

.... (1)

(c) Why do most plants characteristically have a green colour?

....

.... (1)

(d) Chlorophyll *a* and chlorophyll *b* are almost identical molecules, both functioning in photosynthesis. How do the absorption spectra of the two differ?

....

....

.... (2)

(e) Variegated leaves have non-green, non-photosynthetic parts and such areas may appear pale yellow to dark yellow-orange. Suggest a reason for these facts with regard to energy absorption and utilization.

....

.... (2)

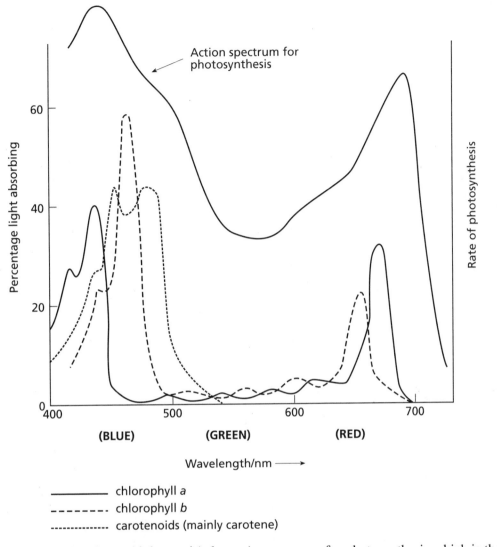

---

chlorophyll *a*
- - - - - - - chlorophyll *b*
-------- carotenoids (mainly carotene)

The diagram also shows (right *y*-axis) the *action spectrum* for photosynthesis which is the amount of photosynthesis occurring in a green plant when illuminated by lights of different wavelengths (but of equal intensity).

(f) Suggest one suitable method of measuring and thus obtaining the experimental results necessary to produce the action spectrum graph.

....

.... (1)

(g) Describe the relationship between the absorption spectrum and the action spectrum.

....

....

....

.... (2)

(h) Briefly indicate what role carotenoid pigments in plastids are thought to play in photosynthesis.

....

....

.... (2)

(i) If, in the laboratory, you wish to extract chlorophyll pigments, you will need to use an organic solvent such as ether (ethoxyethane) or acetone (propanone). Such substances also dissolve lipids. Relate these two pieces of information to explain briefly why such a solvent is necessary in the extraction of the pigments.

....

....

....

.... (2)

Oxford

4   The diagram summaries the light-dependent reaction in photosynthesis.

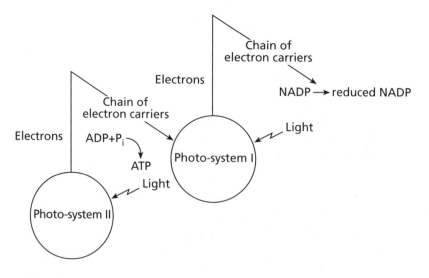

(a) Where, in the chloroplast, does the light-dependent reaction take place?

.... (1)

(b) During this reaction water molecules are broken down to yield oxygen, electrons and hydrogen ions (protons).

   (i) What is the name given to the process in which the water molecules are broken down?

   .... (1)

(ii) What happens to the electrons produced in this process?

....

.... (1)

(iii) What happens to the hydrogen ions?

....

.... (1)

AEB

QUESTIONS

5 Methylene blue can act as a hydrogen acceptor. It is blue in its normal oxidised state but goes colourless when it is reduced by accepting hydrogen atoms.

methylene blue   +   hydrogen   →   reduced methylene blue
  blue colour   colourless

Three test tubes were set up as shown below.

Tube A	Tube B	Tube C
2 cm³ yeast suspension 2 cm³ glucose solution 1 cm³ methylene blue	2 cm³ distilled water 2 cm³ glucose solution 1 cm³ methylene blue	2 cm³ yeast suspension 2 cm³ distilled water 1 cm³ methylene blue

All three tubes were incubated at a temperature of 30 °C. The colour was recorded at the start and after intervals of 5 and 15 minutes. The results are shown in the table.

Colour of contents	Tube A	Tube B	Tube C
at start	blue	blue	blue
after 5 minutes	colourless	blue	blue
after 15 minutes	colourless	blue	pale blue

(a) Explain how tube **B** acted as a control.

....

.... (1)

(b) Suggest an explanation for the colour change after 15 minutes in:

(i) tube **A**;

....

....

.... (2)

(ii) tube **C**.

....

.... (1)

(c) After 20 minutes, tube **A** was shaken vigorously. Use your knowledge of respiration to suggest why the methylene blue turned blue in colour as a result of this treatment.

....

....

.... (2)

AEB

6 (a) The following data are the results of a bubbler experiment using *Elodea* (Canadian pondweed).

Distance between light source and *Elodea* (cm)	Number of bubbles of gas given off per minute
50	8
45	12
40	18
35	24
30	32
25	45
20	59
15	60
10	59

(i) The experiment was designed to investigate the effect of one variable on the rate of photosynthesis.

Which variable was being investigated?

.... (1)

(ii) State one precaution that would have to be taken to ensure that one other possible variable remained constant throughout the experiment.

....

.... (1)

(iii) Give a reason for the relatively uniform rate of bubbling recorded for the three shortest distances.

.... (1)

(iv) The experiment was repeated first with a red light filter and then with a green light filter. Each was inserted, in turn, between the light source and the plant. For each filter, state what you would expect to happen to the rates of bubbling.

Red filter ....

Green filter .... (1)

(b) A population of the alga *Chlorella* was contained in a reaction vessel and illuminated. The concentration of labelled carbon dioxide in the vessel was suddenly reduced at time T as shown in the graph below.

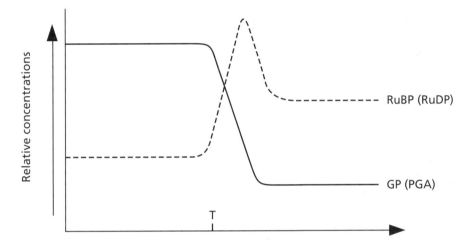

Using the information provided in the graph, explain the relationship between GP (PGA) and RuBP (RuDP) in photosynthesis occurring after time T.

....

.... (2)

SEB

2 *The cell*

The cell and its structure

❶ The **cell theory** states that cells are the smallest units of life and that all cells come from pre-existing cells by cell division. There are two types of cell; **prokaryotes** and **eukaryotes**.

❷ Multicellular organisms have at least two advantages over unicellular organisms: (a) cell specialisation allows them to adapt to a greater variety of environmental demands; (b) they have an increased area of selectively permeable membrane, which enables them to increase control over interactions with their environment.

❸ The selectively permeable membrane of cells is the **plasma membrane**. Its structure is described as a **fluid-mosaic** and is composed of two layers of **phospholipid** molecules positioned with their **hydrophilic** heads outwards and their **hydrophobic** tails inwards. There are protein molecules scattered among the lipids, forming a mosaic. Channels are formed from proteins and allow some materials to cross the membrane. Carbohydrates may be attached to the outer surface of the membrane and the **microtrabecular lattice** may be attached to its inner surface.

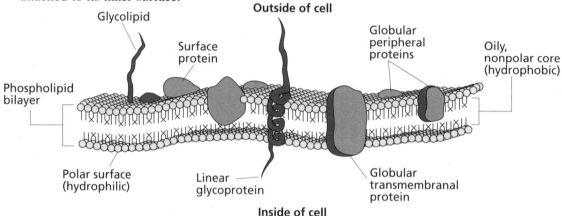

❹ The microtrabecular lattice is a network of **microtubules** and **microfilaments** that forms the internal skeleton of the cell on which **organelles** and some enzymes are attached.

❺ Plant cells have a firm, non-living, permeable **cellulose cell wall**.

❻ Cells have **mitochondria**, which are sometimes called the 'power plants' of the cell because most energy is generated inside them. The most active cells have the most mitochondria.

❼ Cells contain a membranous structure called an **endoplasmic reticulum.** Sometimes **ribosomes**, involved in protein synthesis, are scattered over its surface. This is called **rough** endoplasmic reticulum. In contrast, **smooth** endoplasmic reticulum packages proteins in small sacs for internal cellular use and for export. The endoplasmic reticulum provides a connection of pathways between the **nucleus** and the cell's environment.

❽ There are stacks of flattened vesicles called the **Golgi body**. They package and store materials produced in other organelles and manufacture **polysaccharides**.

❾ Digestive enzymes that control intracellular digestion are stored in small packets called **lysosomes**.

❿ Plant cells contain **plastids**. Colourless plastids called **leucoplasts** store materials. Coloured plastids contain pigments: the best known are the chloroplasts, which contain chlorophyll for photosynthesis.

⓫ **Vacuoles** are fluid-filled sacs and are involved in metabolism and storage. **Contractile vacuoles** are characteristic of unicellular organisms and are specialised for water regulation by pumping out water that has entered due to **endosmosis**.

⓬ Microtubules are made of the protein **tubulin** and form **spindles** during cell division as well as the core of **flagella** and **cilia**.

⑬ Other structures associated with cell division are **centrioles**. They are not found in the cells of flowering plants but are present in the cells of animals, algae and some fungi.

⑭ Hair-like extensions called cilia and flagella are composed of nine pairs of microtubules surrounding a central pair of microtubules. They are used for locomotion in some unicellular organisms and for creating currents with their beating movements in certain tissues of multicellular species.

⑮ Regulation of cellular activities is possible because of the nucleus. It contains genetic material (**chromatin**) and one or more **nucleoli** containing DNA, RNA and protein. The role of the nucleus in cell division enables reproduction to take place.

⑯ Movement of materials in and out of cells takes place passively or actively. There are four types of passive transport:

- **Diffusion**, the movement of molecules from an area of high concentration to one of lower concentration, occurs because molecules are always in constant motion.
- **Facilitated diffusion** is similar to diffusion except that the substances are transported across membranes by enzymes called **permeases**.
- **Bulk flow** is the mass movement of fluids from an area of greater water potential to an area of lesser **water potential**.
- **Osmosis** is the diffusion of water across a selectively permeable membrane from an area of higher water potential to an area of lower water potential until dynamic equilibrium occurs.

⑰ **Active transport** requires the expenditure of energy. One type uses carrier molecules. The ingestion of solids is termed **phagocytosis**. If liquids pass actively it is called **pinocytosis**. Both involve the surrounding of material by the cell membrane, which is then pinched off into vacuoles. The reverse process, **exocytosis**, actively moves substances out of the cell.

The cell and its cycle

❶ During the process of growth cells divide by **mitosis**. Two **daughter cells** are formed with the same number of **chromosomes** as the parent cell.

❷ At the resting stage, or **interphase**, the strands of genetic material double while they prepare for division.

❸ Mitosis has four stages. During the first stage (**prophase**), the nuclear membrane disintegrates, the spindle forms and strands of chromatin condense, forming chromosomes. Each chromosome is composed of two **chromatids** connected by a **centromere**. In the second stage (**metaphase**), the chromosomes line up in the centre of the spindle. During the third stage (**anaphase**), the centromeres split and the chromatids (now called chromosomes) separate and move to opposite ends of the cell. At the fourth stage (**telophase**), the chromosomes unwind and form strands. The nuclear membrane re-forms and division of the cytoplasm occurs. In plant cells a new cell wall forms between the groups of chromosomes. Animal cells pinch in between the groups of chromosomes and form a new cell membrane between them.

❹ There is a type of cell division that halves the chromosome number. It is called **meiosis** and occurs in **gamete** formation. The gametes contain one member of each **homologous pair**, in contrast to body cells, which contain matched pairs of chromosomes, called **homologues**. In animals, gametes are produced in the **gonads** (**ovaries** and **testes**). The typical chromosome number (**diploid**) is restored at **fertilisation** when two gametes, each with half the number of chromosomes (**haploid**), fuse.

❺ In the interphase of meiosis the chromosomes replicate and, therefore, consist of two chromatids connected by a centromere. There are two cell divisions in meiosis. During the first prophase, the chromatin forms chromosomes, the nuclear membrane disintegrates and the spindle starts to form. In contrast to mitosis, the homologous pairs of chromosomes, each consisting of two chromatids, pair up exactly, **allele** to allele. Portions of **DNA**

(**deoxyribonucleic acid**) can be exchanged between the homologues during a process called **crossing over**. This produces essential genetic **variation**. During the first metaphase, in contrast to mitosis, the chromosomes line up on the spindle in homologous pairs. In the first anaphase, members of homologous pairs separate and move to opposite ends of the cell. During the first telophase, the chromosomes become longer and the nuclear membrane re-forms. The chromosomes do not replicate in the second interphase. The events in the second series of stages in meiosis are similar to those of mitosis. At the end of the second series of stages, four cells, each with half the chromosome complement (haploid), are present.

❻ There are two significant points concerning meiosis. It creates haploid gametes and it increases genetic variation because of mixing maternal and paternal genes.

❼ A chromosome is made of protein and DNA, which is a **nucleic acid** containing the sugar **deoxyribose**. DNA is composed of a chain of **nucleotide** pairs in a ladder-like arrangement. The sugar and phosphate of the nucleotides form the sides of a ladder and bases form the rungs. Each rung contains one **purine** (**adenine** or **guanine**) and one **pyrimidine** (**thymine** or **cytosine**). The sequence of bases along each strand is variable, but adenine is always paired to thymine and guanine to cytosine. The entire ladder is twisted into a **double helix**.

❽ During **replication**, the two strands of DNA unwind and open up so that the bases are exposed to the nuclear sap. Nucleotide bases in the sap attach to the appropriate bases of the open strand (adenine to thymine and cytosine to guanine), making two new molecules exactly like the original.

❾ Enzymes are proteins and nucleic acids are used in their manufacture inside cells. First, **RNA** (**ribonucleic acid**) is made, as directed by a portion of DNA. The DNA unwinds and separates between the hydrogen bonds that hold the bases together, as in replication. RNA differs from DNA because RNA contains the sugar **ribose** and the base **uracil** replaces thymine. **Messenger RNA** (**mRNA**) is formed from the DNA, and carries the message of DNA in its sequence of bases to the cytoplasm.

❿ The **genetic code** is used to translate the linear sequence of bases in DNA into a sequence of amino acids used to make proteins.

A sequence of three bases, called a **codon**, codes for an amino acid. Sixty-one of the possible sixty-four codons code for specific amino acids. Three (UAA, UAG and UGA) signal the end of a message. AUG signals the start of a message.

⓫ mRNA forms a complex with a ribosome in the cytoplasm. Amino acids are brought to the complex by a **transfer RNA** (**tRNA**). At one end of each type of tRNA is a sequence of three bases called the **anticodon**, which specifies a particular amino acid. The tRNA positions an amino acid only where it encounters three complementary bases (a codon) in the mRNA. When the amino acid has attached to the growing protein chain, the tRNA moves away. The sequence of bases on mRNA is read three at a time and it determines the sequence of amino acids in a protein, which may be structural or an enzyme.

**If you need to
revise this
subject more
thoroughly,
see the relevant
topics in the
Letts A level
*Biology
Study Guide.***

1 (a) Explain concisely how you could proceed to isolate mitochondria from the cells of a living tissue such as liver.

....

....

....

.... (2)

(b) Having obtained a suitable sample of mitochondria, briefly describe how you could demonstrate any one of their functions experimentally.

....

.... (2)

(c)

(i) Name structure X shown on the above diagram of a mitochondrion.

X .... (1)

(ii) Suggest a suitable average *width* (Y on the diagram) of a mitochondrion as would be found in a typical cell.

Y .... (1)

(iii) On the diagram, which letter, A, B, C, D, or E, best indicates the site of:

glycolysis; ....

Krebs cycle (citric acid cycle) reactions; ....

the cytochrome chain reactions (electron transport chain)? .... (3)

21

(iv) Name an organic molecule (or ion) which enters the mitochondrion.

....

Name an organic molecule which leaves the mitochondrion.

.... (2)

(v) Briefly explain the role of oxygen in the final stages of (aerobic) respiration.

....

.... (2)

Oxford

2 The table below shows, in arbitrary units, the concentration of potassium ions and the sugar consumption in excised roots at different oxygen concentrations of the bathing fluid.

Oxygen percentage	0	2	5	10	20	30	50	70
Potassium ion concentration	7	10	21	49	52	51	49	47
Rate of sugar consumption	14	16	20	27	33	34	35	38

(a) Plot two curves using the same axes, on the squared paper below, to show the relationship between potassium ion concentration in the roots and sugar consumption at the different oxygen concentrations. (8)

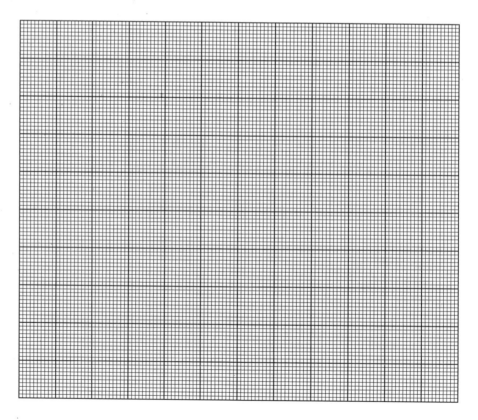

(b) Give an explanation for each of the following:

(i) potassium ions are present in the root even at zero concentration of oxygen;

....

....

.... (2)

(ii) potassium ion concentration increases rapidly with increasing oxygen concentration up to 20;

....

....

.... (2)

(iii) the potassium ion concentration begins to fall off after the peak at oxygen concentration of 20;

....

....

.... (2)

(iv) the rate of sugar consumption continues with increase in oxygen concentration throughout the range shown.

....

....

.... (1)

Oxford

3 The diagrams represent a phospholipid molecule.

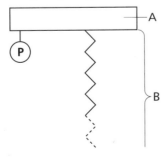

P=phosphate-containing group

Simplified diagram

(a) (i) Name the parts of the molecule labelled **A** and **B**.

A ....

B .... (2)

(ii) How do these two parts of the molecule differ in their properties with respect to water?

....

.... (1)

(b) (i) Use the simplified diagram of this molecule to illustrate how phospholipid molecules are arranged in cell membranes.

(1)

(ii) Explain *one* way in which evidence from electronmicrographs would support the arrangement that you have shown.

....

....

.... (2)
AEB

4   The diagram shows part of an animal cell and is based on a series of electron micrographs.

(a) (i) Name the structures labelled

A ....

B ....

C ....

D .... (4)

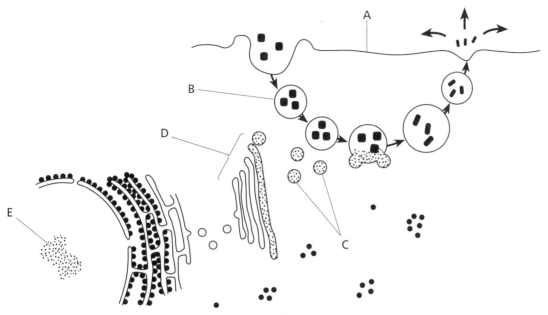

(ii) Label with the letter **F** a structure where the protein contents of **D** are synthesized.

(1)

(iii) What is the part played by **E** in the synthesis of this protein?

....

....

.... (2)

(iv) Describe *one* function **D** may have in the cell.

.... (1)

(b) (i) Name the process illustrated in the diagram which results in large particles entering the cell.

.... (1)

(ii) This process is common in some types of white blood cell. State one reason why this cell activity is important to the body.

.... (1)

WJEC

5 The electron micrograph overleaf shows part of the epithelial cell from the lining of the human small intestine.

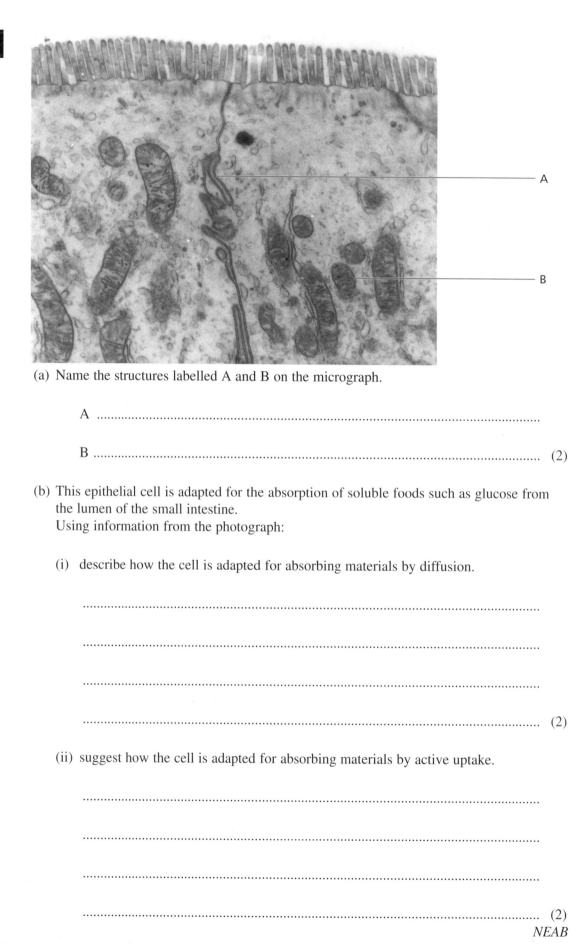

(a) Name the structures labelled A and B on the micrograph.

A ....

B .... (2)

(b) This epithelial cell is adapted for the absorption of soluble foods such as glucose from
the lumen of the small intestine.
Using information from the photograph:

(i) describe how the cell is adapted for absorbing materials by diffusion.

....

....

....

.... (2)

(ii) suggest how the cell is adapted for absorbing materials by active uptake.

....

....

....

.... (2)

NEAB

6 The table below refers to a liver cell, a palisade mesophyll cell and a bacterium (prokaryotic cell) and structures which may be found in them.

If the structure is present, place a tick (✓) in the appropriate box and if the structure is absent, place a cross (✗) in the appropriate box.

Structure	Liver cell	Palisade cell	Bacterium
Nuclear envelope			
Cell wall			
Microvilli			
Chloroplasts			

(4)

ULEAC

7 (a) In the space below make a labelled diagram to show the structure of a typical bacterium as revealed by the electron microscope. Label clearly any **six** important features.

(6)

(b) Give two reasons why the organism you have shown in (a) is described as **prokaryotic.**

1 ....

2 .... (2)

Oxford

3 *Life processes*

Respiration, circulation and nutrition

❶ Breathing is the physical process resulting in exchange of gases at a breathing surface. **Respiration** is the chemical release of energy in every living cell.

❷ Small aquatic invertebrates have enough surface area in relation to their volume for an adequate amount of oxygen to diffuse to all cells. Larger aquatic animals like fish have **gills**, which are thin-walled projections that create a large surface for gaseous exchange via an extensive blood system.

Many invertebrates have cilia that set up a current of water over a breathing surface to improve gaseous exchange. Insects have a specialized system of tubes called **tracheae**, which supply internal cells directly with air.

❸ Breathing in mammals occurs in **lungs**. During ventilation air moves through the windpipe (**trachea**) to the smaller **bronchi**, to the branching **bronchioles** and finally to the air sacs (**alveoli**).

❹ A circulatory system carries oxygen, nutrients, hormones and waste products around the body. Smaller invertebrates distribute materials by diffusion.

❺ Some invertebrates, like molluscs and arthropods, have an **open** circulatory system where blood leaves the vessels and bathes the organ systems.

❻ Vertebrates have **closed** circulatory systems, with a large muscular **heart** that pumps blood through **arteries** to **arterioles** and to thin-walled **capillaries** where exchange of materials between the blood and cells occurs via **lymph**. Capillaries join up to form **venules**, which form **veins**, which return the blood to the heart.

❼ Nitrogenous wastes are removed from the blood by the excretory system. Most carbon dioxide passes into the red blood cells and forms carbonic acid, creating hydrogen ions and hydrogencarbonate ions. Sodium hydrogencarbonate is eventually formed and passes to the **lungs** where it is broken down to carbon dioxide, which is exhaled.

❽ The heart is a muscular pump for moving blood. Its structure varies among invertebrates. In vertebrates there is an evolutionary progression from a two-chambered structure in a fish to a four-chambered structure in a mammal.

The fish-like condition allows for a **single** circulation in which the blood passes once through the heart on its way around the body. Mammals and birds have a **double** circulation, in which the blood passes twice through the heart during its circulation.

❾ Heart rate decreases when the arteries are stretched by an increased volume of blood and the heart rate increases when the veins are stretched by an increase in blood volume. Heart rate also changes in response to blood carbon dioxide and oxygen levels or to emotional stress. The nervous system can also dilate some arteries, depending on the immediate needs of the body.

❿ The **lymphatic** system is a second circulatory system. It circulates lymph, which is part of the fluid constituent of the blood that has filtered through the walls of capillaries to bathe the body cells. The lymph is then collected in **lymph vessels**, which may bring it to **lymph nodes**, where bacteria and cellular debris are filtered out. **Lymphocytes** are a type of white blood cell abundant in lymph nodes; they can attack and destroy bacteria.

⓫ Food supplies energy for metabolism and building blocks for growth. **Digestion** reduces the molecular size of nutrients so that they can be absorbed into the blood system for transport to body cells.

⓬ *Amoeba* and some of the other single-celled animals engulf their food by **phagocytosis**. They digest their food in bubble-like vacuoles. In Cnidaria and flatworms digestion begins extracellularly in a cavity, and is completed in cells that absorb partially-digested particles from the cavity.

⑬ In more complex animals, the digestive system is a tube with two openings. In mammals, digestion begins in the mouth. Food then moves through the **oesophagus** to the **stomach**, where digestion continues. Next the food enters the **small intestine**, where digestion is completed using secretions from the **pancreas** and from the walls of the **ileum**. Undigested material is egested via the **anus**. Food is moved along the digestive system by waves of muscular contractions called **peristalsis**.

⑭ An important chemical process in digestion is **hydrolysis**, the breakdown of molecules by the addition of water.

⑮ Hydrolysis begins in the mouth, where digestion of starch to maltose by the enzyme **amylase** occurs. Protein digestion begins in the stomach with the action of **pepsin**, which breaks down large protein molecules into smaller **peptones** and **proteoses**. In the **duodenum**, the food mixes with the enzymes amylase, which continues starch digestion, **trypsin**, which continues protein digestion, and **lipase**, which begins fat digestion. Digestion is completed by the secretions of the ileum and the products are absorbed into the **villi** of the small intestine. The villi have many other projections from their surface, called **microvilli**, which greatly increase the surface area for absorption.

⑯ Digestive enzymes from the pancreas are secreted in an inactive form so that they will not digest the alimentary canal. A protective layer of mucus is also secreted for similar protection of the stomach and intestinal linings.

⑰ **Bile** emulsifies fats so that there is an increased surface area for the fat-digesting lipase to act. It is made in the **liver** and is stored in the **gall bladder**. Bile mixes with the food in the duodenum.

⑱ The absorbed products of digestion are carried to the liver in the **hepatic portal vein** for storing, sorting and distributing.

⑲ The remaining materials enter the **large intestine**, which consists of the **colon** and **rectum**. Water is absorbed from this material and forms **faeces**, which are stored in the rectum before leaving the alimentary canal via the anus.

Support and muscular systems

❶ **Exoskeletons** support the body from the outside and **endoskeletons** do the same from the inside. Soft-bodied invertebrates have muscles that contract against body fluids, creating pressure, which forms a **hydrostatic skeleton**.

❷ Exoskeletons may restrict growth unless they are capable of growing with the animal, as happens in molluscs. Arthropods cast off their old skeletons before growing new ones.

❸ **Connective tissues** are supporting tissues. The nature of the tissue depends on the composition of the **matrix**, which is a non-living material secreted by cells and makes up most of the tissue. Bone matrix consists of salts of calcium and potassium and is made flexible by having the protein **collagen** throughout. Larger bones have cavities filled with **marrow**. **Yellow marrow** is composed mainly of fat cells, but **red marrow** is the centre of manufacture of red and white blood cells.

❹ Bone is made of **Haversian systems**. In the centre of each Haversian system is a canal with the blood supply for the bone cells that are arranged in concentric circles around it. The cells, which lie in the spaces in the matrix, extend through tiny canals called **canaliculi**, allowing organic contact between them. There is a constant turnover of matrix as **osteoclasts** withdraw salts of potassium and calcium from the matrix and **osteoblasts** deposit new matrix.

❺ **Ligaments** are made of **elastic** connective tissue and hold bones together. **Tendons** are non-elastic cords that anchor muscles to bones.

6 The vertebrate skeleton is divided into the **axial skeleton** and the **appendicular skeleton**. The axial skeleton forms the axis of the body and includes the **skull**, **vertebral column** and, in vertebrates higher than the fish, **sternum** and **ribs**. The appendicular skeleton includes the limb bones and the limb girdles.

7 Bones can move in relation to one another at **joints**. Different types of joint allow different degrees of movement. **Ball-and-socket** joints provide the greatest amount of movement. **Hinge** joints permit movement in one plane. There is little flexibility in the **pubic symphysis** and in the bones of the skull, where they meet at **fused** joints.

8 There are three types of vertebrate muscle: **smooth**, **cardiac**, and **skeletal**. Involuntary muscle includes smooth muscle, which is found in the walls of many internal organ systems, and cardiac muscle, which is unique to the heart. Skeletal muscles are under voluntary control and, together with cardiac muscle, have visible striations.

9 Each skeletal muscle is a bundle of millions of muscle cells (**fibres**), each bound by connective tissue and surrounded by a further layer of tough connective tissue. Most skeletal muscles are attached to bones by tendons. When a muscle contracts, the bone providing the surface for the muscle's **insertion** moves closer to the more stationary bone – the one providing the surface for the muscle's **origin**.

10 Skeletal muscles are normally arranged in **antagonistic pairs** of **flexors** and **extensors**, whose contractions pull in opposite directions and sometimes generate the tension between them needed for posture.

11 Each skeletal muscle cell contains several nuclei and many smaller **myofibrils**. Each myofibril is made of even smaller **myofilaments**. The arrangement of the myofilaments gives the muscle its striated appearance.

  The myofilaments are made of two proteins called **actin** and **myosin**.

12 According to the **sliding filament theory**, a muscle contracts when actin filaments slide towards one another, past the myosin filaments. The movement occurs because projections from the myosin filaments, called **bridges**, attach to actin filaments and pull them towards the centre of the contractile unit. The bridges then release the actin, reach out, and reattach to other actin filaments, pulling them along in a ratchet-like fashion. Myosin cross-bridges attach to actin only when calcium ions are present to open attachment sites along the actin filament. The energy in ATP is needed to break the cross-bridge, freeing it to attach further along the actin molecule.

If you need to revise this subject more thoroughly, see the relevant topics in the *Letts* A level Biology Study Guide.

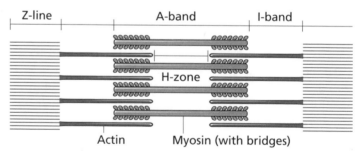

Arrangement of actin and myosin myofilaments (relaxed)

Z-line   A-band   I-band

H-zone

Actin   Myosin (with bridges)

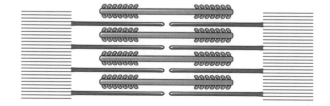

Arrangement of actin and myosin myofilaments (contracted)

1   The llama is a goat-like mammal which lives at altitudes of 5000 m in the South American Andes. The table below shows the effect of varying the partial pressure of oxygen on the % saturation of haemoglobin from a llama and from a goat which lives at sea level.

Partial pressure of oxygen (mm Hg)	% saturation of haemoglobin	
	llama	goat
0	0	0
20	60	15
40	86	55
60	95	80
80	100	94
100	100	100

(a) Using the same axis plot oxygen dissociation curves for the haemoglobin of both of these animals on the graph paper below.

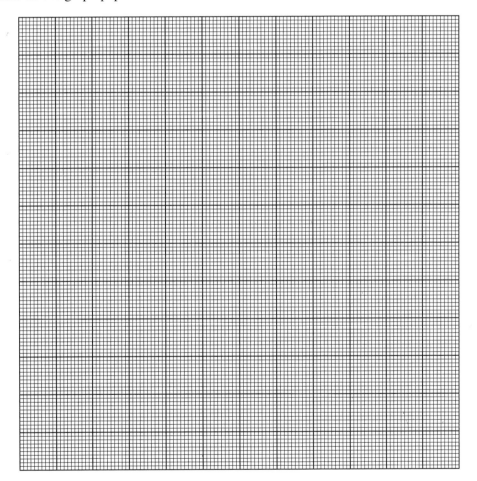

(4)

(b) The graph below shows how the partial pressure of oxygen varies with altitude.

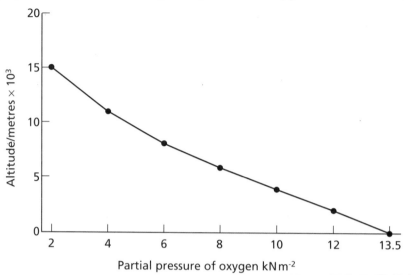

The oxygen dissociation curve for the haemoglobin of the goat is typical of most mammals which live at low altitudes. Explain as fully as you can the advantage to the llama in having a different oxygen dissociation curve for its haemoglobin.

....

....

....

.... (4)

NEAB

2   The heart has a 'natural pace-maker' which controls the rhythm of the heart beat. The diagram below shows how impulses spread from the natural pace-maker to the rest of the heart. The times shown are relative to a time of 0 seconds when an impulse is initiated at the sino-atrial node.

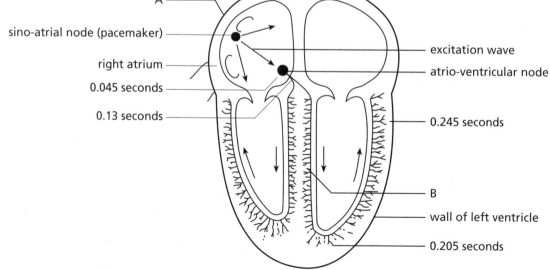

(a) Name the parts labelled A and B on the diagram.

A ....

B .... (2)

(b) Explain the pattern of impulses shown by the times indicated on the diagram.

....

....

....

.... (2)

(c) Some people have a heart which beats in an irregular way. This may be due to faults in the natural pace-maker or to faults in the nerves which lead to this natural pace-maker. An artificial pace-maker produces a regular impulse. It is inserted under the skin of the chest and connected to a thin lead which passes through a vein in the neck and down to the right ventricle of the heart.

    (i) Suggest, by marking clearly with an X on the diagram, where the electrode on the end of the lead should be positioned in the right ventricle.

    (ii) Explain the reason for your choice.

       ....

       ....

       ....

       .... (3)

(d) During exercises there is an increase in the carbon dioxide content of the blood. Describe how this increase is detected and how the detection eventually leads to an increase in the rate of heart beat.

....

....

....

.... (4)

NEAB

QUESTIONS

3 Dye can be injected into the vein of a human at the point indicated in the diagram. The amount of dye in the blood is sampled by drawing off a sample from the position shown at second intervals. The amount of dye in the sample can be measured using a machine called a colorimeter. The graph shows the concentration of dye at point **S** for a person at rest and exercising.

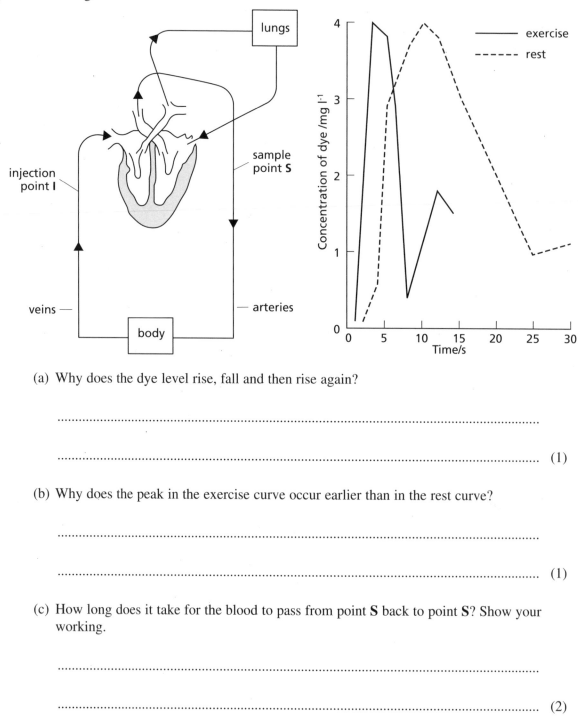

(a) Why does the dye level rise, fall and then rise again?

....

.... (1)

(b) Why does the peak in the exercise curve occur earlier than in the rest curve?

....

.... (1)

(c) How long does it take for the blood to pass from point **S** back to point **S**? Show your working.

....

.... (2)

(d) Cardiac output is a measure of the volume of blood pumped by the heart in a unit time.

(i) If the heart beats at 70 beats/min at rest with a stroke volume of 80 cm³, what is the cardiac output per minute in litres?

....

.... (2)

(ii) After heavy exercise the heart rate increased to 170 beats/min. If the cardiac output was 25 litres/min, what was the stroke volume? Show your working.

....

.... (2)

Oxford

4 The diagram below shows a longitudinal section of part of the ileum wall.

(a) Name the structures labelled A, B and C.

A ....

B ....

C .... (3)

QUESTIONS

(b) Describe *one* way in which the structure of the ileum is adapted to the function it performs.

....

....

.... (2)

ULEAC

5 Diagram 1 represents a longitudinal section through striated muscle.

Diagram 1

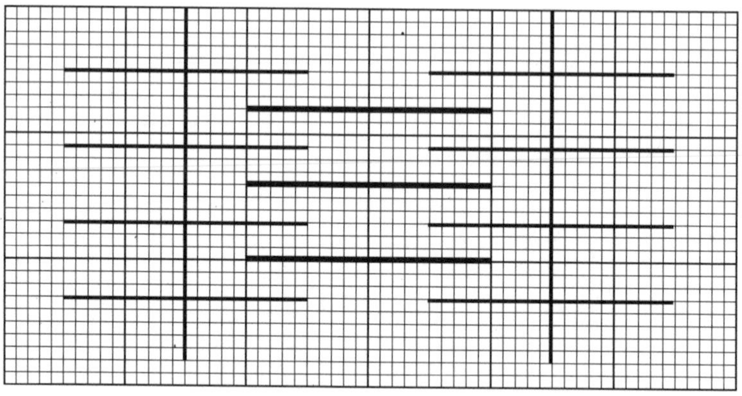

(a) Draw a similar diagram to represent the appearance of the same section when the muscle has contracted. (2)

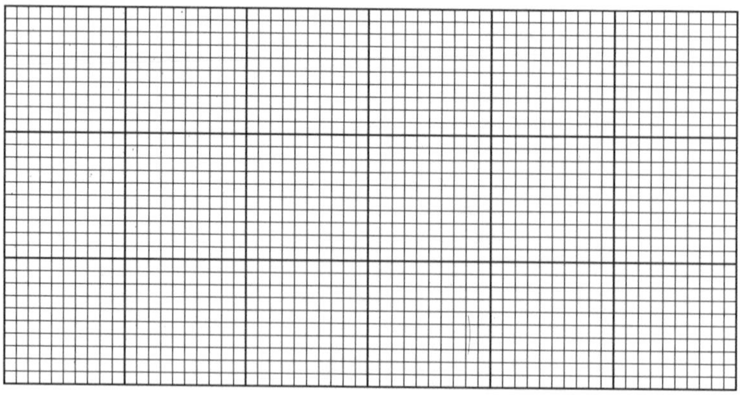

(b) Diagram 2 represents a cross-section through this muscle.

Diagram 2

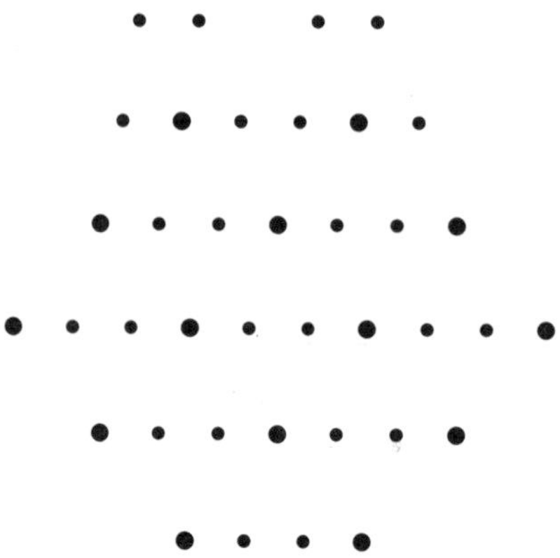

Draw a vertical line on Diagram 1 to show from where the cross-section might have been taken. (1)

(c) Describe the part played in the contraction of striated muscle by:

(i) calcium ions;

....

.... (1)

(ii) the energy released from the breakdown of ATP.

....

....(1)

AEB

6 The drawing has been made from a slide of skeletal muscle tissue seen with a light microscope at a magnification of 800 times. It shows parts of two motor units.

Motor end plate

Motor nerve fibres

Skeletal muscle fibres

(a) Use evidence from the drawing to suggest:

(i) a meaning for the term *motor unit*;

.... (1)

(ii) why all the muscle fibres shown will not necessarily contract at the same time.

.... (1)

QUESTIONS

(b) Briefly describe the sequence of events at the motor end plate which leads to an action potential passing along the muscle fibre.

....

....

.... (3)

The diagram shows the pathways by which energy is produced for muscle contraction. Numbers **1** to **3** indicate the order in which the various pathways are called on to supply ATP as muscular effort increases.

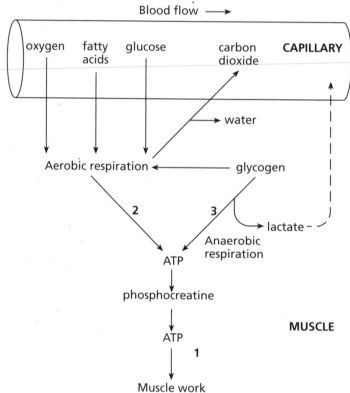

(c) (i) What happens to the lactate produced in pathway **3**?

....

....

.... (3)

(ii) Explain the part played by phosphocreatine in supplying energy to the muscle.

....

.... (2)

Most muscles contain both slow twitch and fast twitch fibres, but the proportion of each depends on the function of the muscle as a whole. The table below lists some differences between slow twitch and fast twitch fibres.

Characteristic	Slow twitch fibre	Fast twitch fibre
Contraction time/milliseconds	110	50
Mitochondria	Many present	Relatively few
Glycogen store	Low	High
Myosin ATPase activity	Low	High
Capillaries	Many present	Fewer present
Sarcoplasmic reticulum	Poorly developed	Well developed
Rate of fatigue	Slow	Fast

(d) Suggest why muscles concerned with maintaining the posture of the body might be expected to have a large proportion of slow twitch fibres.

....

.... (2)

(e) Explaining your answer in each case, give *two* pieces of evidence from the table which:

(i) suggest that fast twitch fibres may easily build up an oxygen debt;

....

....

....

.... (4)

(ii) might account for the difference in speed of contraction of the two types of fibre.

....

....

....

.... (4)

AEB

4 *Co-ordination*

The senses

❶ All species are sensitive to **stimuli** (changes in the surroundings) and respond in such a way that it is to their advantage.

❷ **Receptors** contain nerve cells capable of detecting stimuli.

❸ In many mammals temperature is detected by receptors for warmth, cold and very high temperatures causing pain. The receptors are unevenly distributed over the body.

❹ **Tactile receptors** respond to touch. Invertebrates have such receptors and vertebrates have **Pacinian corpuscles**, which respond to pressure and **Meissner's corpuscles**, which respond to touch. These sense organs are in the skin.

❺ Most invertebrates cannot hear, as such, using **auditory receptors**, but some insects have **tympanal membranes** that respond to sound waves. In mammals, the **external ear** collects sound waves and funnels them to the **eardrum**. The resulting vibrations of the eardrum are carried through the bones of the middle ear; the hammer (**malleus**), anvil (**incus**) and stirrup (**stapes**). The vibrations of the bones cause the **oval window** to vibrate and this causes fluid in the **cochlea** to move. Movement of the fluid causes the **basilar membrane** to vibrate and push cilia on its surface into the overlying **tectorial membrane**, initiating nerve impulses. The pitch of the sound is registered according to which hairs are stimulated. Loudness is encoded in the number of neurons responding to the sound and the frequency of impulses.

❻ The senses of smell and taste are brought about as a result of chemical stimuli in solution. In mammals, **olfactory receptors** in the nasal cavity are connected to the brain's **olfactory lobes**. There are four basic tastes: sweet, sour, bitter and salty, each located in a specific region of the tongue. Although receptors generally respond to more that one taste, each is particularly sensitive to one. Invertebrates cannot separate taste from smell and their chemoreception provides information about the environment before interaction with it occurs.

❼ Receptors that detect internal mechanical stimuli are called **proprioceptors**. These sense the position of various parts of the body. They range from those at the base of hairs to those within large bundles of muscle cells. Vertebrate proprioceptors used to detect change in equilibrium and enable orientation are the fluid-filled **semicircular canals**, which open into the **utricle** and **saccule**. Changes in body position cause the fluid to move, which in turn causes small granules to move and stimulate sensory hairs in the utricle and saccule.

❽ Eyes have visual pigments that absorb particular wavelengths of light and change the wave energy into a nerve impulse. The light-sensitive part of the eye is the **retina**. It contains **rods** and **cones**, which are specialised nerve cells that detect light and colour respectively.

Hormones and nerves

❶ A **hormone** is a chemical secreted by an **endocrine gland** directly into the blood, which carries it to the part of the body where it has an effect.

❷ Hormones regulate body processes, prepare the body for stress and help adapt the organism to its environment.

❸ A peptide hormone (first messenger) functions from outside a target cell by binding to a receptor molecule on the cell membrane. This complex binds to an enzyme in the membrane, which then converts ATP to **cyclic AMP**. Cyclic AMP acts as a second messenger by triggering a series of biochemical reactions within the cell.

❹ A steroid hormone functions from within cells. It binds to a receptor in a target cell's cytoplasm. This complex enters the nucleus where it directs the synthesis of specific mRNA. The mRNA moves to the cytoplasm and directs the synthesis of new protein.

⑤ **Negative feedback** systems regulate the production of many hormones. An example is the interaction between tropic hormones and their target cells. The **anterior pituitary gland** secretes **thyroid-stimulating hormone (TSH)**, which causes the **thyroid** to secrete **thyroxine**. A drop in thyroxine levels stimulates TSH secretion, whereas a rise slows TSH secretion.

⑥ The nervous and endocrine systems are related structurally, functionally and chemically.

⑦ Nerve cells (**neurons**) consist of a **cell body**, **dendrites** that receive stimuli from other neurons, and an **axon** that conducts impulses away from the cell body. A fatty **myelin sheath** surrounds some vertebrate axons and increases the speed of impulse transmission. Nerves are bundles of neurons.

⑧ **Glial cells** in the nervous system may function in a variety of ways, e.g. binding and supporting neurons insulating neurons and providing materials for neural transmission.

⑨ An external stimulus is detected by a receptor that is specialised for a particular sensation. The impulse is transferred to an **afferent** (sensory) neuron, which carries it to the **central nervous system**. The impulse is taken away from the central nervous system towards an **effector** (muscle or gland) by an **efferent** (motor) neuron.

⑩ In a resting neuron there are more sodium ions outside the cell membrane than inside, and more potassium ions inside than outside. The inside of the resting neuron has a negative charge due to chloride ions and negatively charged proteins. This distribution of ions creates a **resting potential** of about 70 millivolts. The resting neuron's membrane is not very permeable to sodium ions. If sodium ions leak into the cell they are pumped out by the **sodium-potassium pump**.

⑪ A nerve impulse begins when the membrane suddenly becomes permeable to sodium ions at some point along the membrane, and these ions enter the cell through **ion gates**, depolarizing the membrane. A wave of inrushing sodium ions sweeps along the length of the neuron. At the point along the membrane where sodium ions enter, the interior of the neuron becomes temporarily positive. However, the membrane is immediately repolarized as potassium ions leave the cell. The change in distribution of charge that sweeps along the neuron is called an **action potential**.

⑫ Any stimulus of at least **threshold** value initiates an impulse, which does not lose strength as it travels along the cell. The brain interprets the intensity of a stimulus as either frequency of impulses or the number of neurons stimulated.

⑬ The point where one neuron meets another is called a **synapse**. At the axon tip, an impulse triggers the release of a neurotransmitter from small storage packets. This chemical crosses the gap between neurons. If a chemical comes from an **excitatory** neuron it lowers the threshold of firing in the receiving neuron. If the chemical comes from an **inhibitory** neuron it raises the threshold of firing in the receiving neuron. The neurotransmitter in the gap is quickly neutralised.

If you need to revise this subject more thoroughly, see the relevant topics in the *Letts* **A level** *Biology Study Guide.*

1   The diagram below shows a single rod from a mammalian retina.

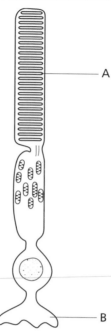

(a) Name the parts labelled A and B and give *one* function of each. Write your answers in the table below.

Part	Name	Function
A		
B		

(4)

(b) Draw an arrow next to the diagram to indicate the direction in which light passes through this cell.

(1)

(c) State *two* ways in which vision using cones differs from vision using rods.

1 ....

2 .... (2)

ULEAC

2   Read through the following passage on adrenal activity, then write on the dotted lines the most appropriate word or words to complete the passage.

ACTH is secreted in irregular bursts throughout the day. In the human, the bursts are most frequent in the early .... and least frequent in the .... This .... rhythm is normally spread over .... hours, but if the light/dark period is lengthened experimentally to more than this, the adrenal cycle is lengthened but the increase in adrenal secretion still occurs during the period of .... The biological clock responsible for the rhythmic secretion of ACTH is located in the ....

(6)

ULEAC

3 (a) The diagram shows a simplified version of the structure of the mammalian ear.

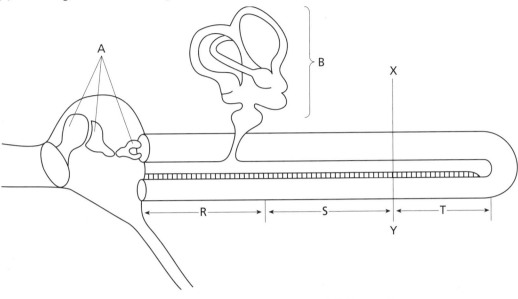

(i) State the function of the structures labelled A and B in the diagram.

A ....

B .... (2)

(ii) Draw a simple diagram to show the appearance of a transverse section of the cochlea along XY. Label *two* structures concerned with converting pressure waves into nerve impulses.

(4)

(b) Suggest how using the earphones of a personal stereo at full volume may result in partial deafness.

....

....

....

.... (2)

WJEC

4 The graph below shows the change in potential difference across the membrane of a neuron.

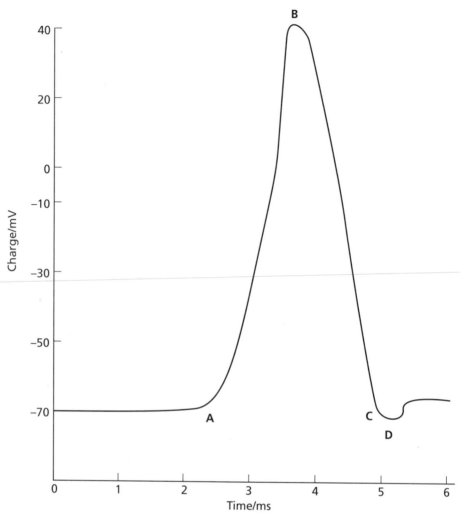

(a) What causes the inside of the membrane to be negatively charged with respect to the outside in the resting condition?

....

....

.... (2)

(b) Explain what has brought about the change in potential between:

(i) A and B;

....

.... (2)

(ii) B and C.

....

.... (2)

(c) What is the cause and the reason for the drop in potential difference below the resting potential at D?

Cause .... (1)

Reason .... (1)

(d) How could the size of B be increased in an experimental situation?

....

....

.... (2)

Oxford

5 Segments from the stem internodes of young pea seedlings were used in an experiment to find the effects of the auxin indole acetic acid (IAA) and gibberellic acid (GA) on elongation of the stem. The stem segments were kept in identical conditions apart from the treatments outlined below.

Control, no plant growth substance (GA and IAA) added
GA only
IAA only
GA and IAA

The results are shown in the graph below.

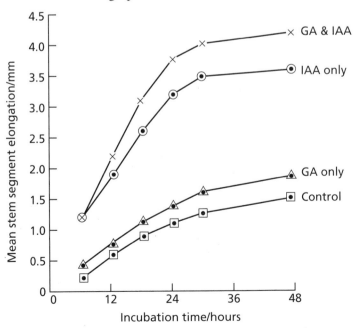

(a) (i) Comment on the effects on the elongation of the stem segments of GA and IAA separately and GA and IAA combined.

....

....

....

....

....

....

.... (4)

(ii) What type of interaction is shown by the two growth substances?

.... (1)

(iii) Over which period of the investigation do the plant growth substances have their greatest effect? Suggest a reason for your answer.

....

....

....

.... (2)

(b) State *two* other effects of IAA in plants, other than stem elongation, and in each case suggest a commercial application.

1 ....

....

2 ....

.... (4)

ULEAC

6 The following diagram shows a section of the human brain.

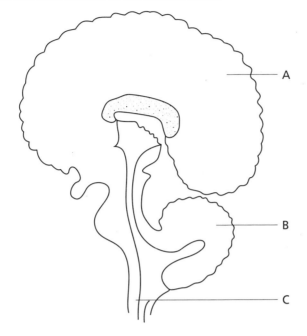

(a) Label the structures A, B and C. (3)

(b) Give *one* function for each of these areas.

A ....

B ....

C .... (3)

(c) What would the effect on a part of the body if:

(i) the spinal nerve from that region was cut?

.... (1)

(ii) the dorsal root of the spinal nerve from that region was cut?

.... (1)

(iii) the ventral root of the spinal nerve from that region was cut?

....

.... (1)

Oxford

5 *Homeostasis*

Regulation

❶ Homeostasis is the tendency of living things to maintain an internal environment within certain limits. This **steady state** is usually maintained by **negative feedback** mechanisms that operate when an increase in a system's product slows the system. In the less common **positive feedback** mechanisms, the system's product increases the activity of the system, generating a constantly accelerating system.

❷ An example of homeostasis is temperature regulation. If living things become very cold, the water within cells may freeze, disrupting cellular constituents. Conversely, very high temperatures denature proteins.

❸ All invertebrates and vertebrates other than mammals and birds lack physiological mechanisms for controlling temperature. Fish, reptiles and amphibians regulate body temperature behaviourally.

❹ Birds and mammals use physiological methods to regulate their temperature. They have fur or feathers for insulation and a four-chambered heart to pump efficiently oxygen-carrying blood that fuels the metabolism needed to maintain a constant body temperature. Body temperature is registered in the brain's **hypothalamus**. Mammals sweat and cool themselves by evaporation. Heat loss is reduced by constriction of surface blood vessels. **Thyroxine** elevates body temperature by increasing the metabolic rate.

❺ All animals must eliminate metabolic wastes, such as those containing nitrogen from the breakdown of proteins. **Natural selection** has resulted in different nitrogen-containing waste products in species with different water conservation needs. **Ammonia**, a common waste product among aquatic invertebrates and fish, is poisonous and requires a great deal of water to dilute it. **Urea** is a waste product of mammals and is less toxic. It can therefore be excreted with less water loss. **Uric acid** is a common waste product of insects and birds. These animals have a particular need to conserve water.

❻ Animals have the problem of regulating their water content while flushing metabolic wastes from the body. Freshwater fish rid themselves of both excess water gained by osmosis and metabolic waste, through **glomeruli** in their **kidneys**. Saltwater animals tend to lose water by osmosis. The kidneys of many saltwater animals have water-conserving adaptations, such as small glomeruli and a method for removing excess salt taken in with sea water.

❼ Different species remove waste by different mechanisms, including diffusion, contractile vacuoles and excretory systems. In some species, problems of metabolic waste and internal water regulations are solved by the same mechanisms, whilst in others they are solved by different mechanisms.

❽ A human kidney consists of approximately one million **nephrons**, each consisting of a glomerulus in a **Bowman's capsule** together with a **tubule**. All but large particles such as proteins and blood cells are filtered from the blood through the thin-walled glomerulus. The filtrate, which contains waste products, water, salts and glucose, enters the cup-like Bowman's capsule that surrounds the glomerulus and begins to flow through the **proximal convoluted tubule**, the **loop of Henle**, and the **distal convoluted tubule**. Blood vessels arise from the glomerulus and surround the tubules. Many usable materials move by diffusion or by active transport from the filtrate within the tubules into the blood vessels. Material remaining in the tubules, primarily urea and water, flows on to collecting ducts leading to the **ureter** and finally to the **bladder**, where it is stored as **urine**.

❾ Water reabsorption from the tubules back to the blood is controlled by **antidiuretic hormone** (**ADH**) from the posterior lobe of the **pituitary gland**. The more ADH secreted, the more concentrated the urine. ADH secretion varies with the osmotic concentration of the blood, which is altered by dietary factors such as water and protein, and is inhibited by ethanol.

The immune system

❶ Defence mechanisms in the body include barriers to invasion, inflammatory responses, fever, phagocytosis and direct attack by **killer cells**.

❷ Barriers that prevent microbes entering the body include the skin and mucous membranes lining surfaces within the body cavity. Cilia often waft mucus containing microbes away from vulnerable areas. The enzyme **lysozyme** together with acid secretions may also defend the body from invasion.

❸ Microbes entering the body trigger **inflammation**. Certain cells secrete **histamine**, which dilates arterioles in the area, causing swelling and redness.
Fever raises the temperature and makes the body unsuitable for certain microbes.

❹ **Phagocytes** are three types of white blood cell that engulf invaders. These types are called **eosinophils**, **neutrophils**, and **monocytes**. Eosinophils respond to allergies and parasites. Neutrophils are the first line of defence at the site of invasion. The monocytes grow and produce large, long-lived **macrophages** that quickly engulf microbes.

❺ Another type of white blood cell, the natural killer cell, breaks the membranes of some types of cancerous cell or cells containing viruses.

❻ Specific diseases are attacked with specific responses. Two types of **lymphocytes**, **B-cells** and **helper T-cells**, are important. B-cells make **antibodies** to fight the invader. They also produce **memory cells** that can defend against invasion by the same organism at a later date. Helper T-cells stimulate the production of (i) cells that attack invaders (**cytotoxic T-cells**) and (ii) memory T-cells.

❼ **Antigens** are foreign molecules that trigger the host's immune responses. Antibodies produced by the host identify and help destroy antigen-bearing cells. Antibody molecules consist of two identical short chains and two identical long chains, arranged in a Y-shape. The arms of the Y-shape determine whether the antigen is attacked. The rest of the antibody is relatively constant and determines how the invader is attacked. Three general ways antibodies attack invaders are by linking invaders together, by marking invaders for attack by phagocytes and by triggering reactions that break up the invading microbes.

❽ After a macrophage destroys an invading cell, it places an antigen-carrying piece of the invader on its own membrane. Then this macrophage moves around the body until it finds a helper T-cell with an antigen-recognition site matching the structure of the invader's antigen attached to its membrane. The antigen and the helper T-cell's antigen-recognition site lock together, triggering the production of a chemical (**interleukin**) that stimulates the production of B-cells and cytotoxic T-cells. Each lymphocyte bears the antigen-recognition site. Cytotoxic T-cells then recognize and destroy body cells infected with the original type of invader. Interleukin also triggers the production of B-cells, which form short-lived **plasma cells** that secrete antibodies specific for the antigen discovered by their parent cell, and memory B-cells, which will quickly form more plasma cells upon subsequent invasion by organisms bearing the original antigen.

❾ The **primary response** begins with the actions of the helper T-cells and is slow. The **secondary response** is triggered by memory cells and is rapid.

❿ A **vaccination** is the injection of an antigen, triggering the production of memory cells against it. When an organism bearing that antigen invades the body, the response is rapid and vigorous.

If you need to revise this subject more thoroughly, see the relevant topics in the *Letts A level Biology Study Guide*.

5 Homeostasis

QUESTIONS

1 Read the following passage and then answer the questions.

One of the important growth-controlling systems in plants is provided by the so-called 'plant growth substances' or 'plant hormones'. A plant growth substance is an organic substance which is produced within a plant which will, at low concentrations, promote, inhibit or modify growth, usually at a site other than its place of origin. Its effect does not depend upon its energy content nor does it depend on its content of essential elements.

One of the difficulties in the study of plant growth substances is that much of it is based on circumstantial evidence derived from experiments in which the chemical, or a closely related substance, is applied to the appropriate plant from the outside. The reasoning in such a case is usually as follows.

A   We know that a substance X, or one very like it, occurs in a certain plant.

B   We have a supply of substance Y, which is very similar to substance X.

C   When applied to the relevant plant, substance Y causes a specific response (for example, stem elongation).

D   Therefore it is likely or possible that substance X has a role in controlling stem elongation in this plant.

Adapted from Hill, Endogenous Plant Growth Substances, Arnold (1973)

(a) The author of this passage used the term 'plant hormone' as an alternative to 'plant growth substance' (line 2). Other authorities reject the term 'plant hormone' on the grounds that the comparison with animal hormones is not valid.

(i) State *two* features that plant growth substances and animal hormones have in common.

1 ....

2 .... (2)

(ii) State *two* differences between plant growth substances and animal hormones.

1 ....

2 .... (2)

(b) (i) Explain why the experimental evidence referred to in the passage (statements A, B, C and D, lines 10 – 15) does not demonstrate conclusively that substance X has a role in controlling stem elongation in the plant concerned.

....

....

.... (3)

(ii) Suggest *two* other pieces of evidence which might be sought to support the conclusion that substance X has a role in controlling stem elongation.

1 ....

....

2 ....

.... (2)

(c) Assume that substance Y can be manufactured cheaply in large quantities. Suggest *two* possible commercial applications that might be investigated for substance Y.

1 ....

....

2 ....

.... (2)

ULEAC

2   The diagram summarises the movement of some substances from the loop of Henle in a nephron from a mammalian kidney.

⬜⇨ Passive movement of water

◻➡ Passive movement of sodium chloride

◼➡ Active transport of chloride ions

(a) Explain why there are large numbers of mitochondria in the cells between points **C** and **D**.

....

.... (2)

(b) (i) Explain how the movement of the substances shown on the diagram produces a change in the concentration of the tubule contents between points **A** and **D**.

....

.... (2)

(ii) Describe the role of the collecting duct in producing urine which is more concentrated than the body fluids.

....

.... (3)

(c) Small mammals living in deserts produce extremely concentrated urine. How is this related to kidney structure and function?

....

.... (2)

The temperature control centre co-ordinates the mechanisms which regulate body temperature.

(d) (i) Where in the brain is the temperature control centre?

.... (1)

(ii) Describe how the temperature control centre detects a rise in body temperature and produces an increase in the rate of sweating.

....

....

.... (3)

The graph opposite shows the fluctuations in the rectal temperature of two camels. Animal **A** was allowed unlimited access to drinking water; Animal **B** was not provided with water.

(e) Explain why rectal temperature was measured rather than skin temperature.

....(1)

(f) Explain the variation in rectal temperature of animal **A**.

....

....(3)

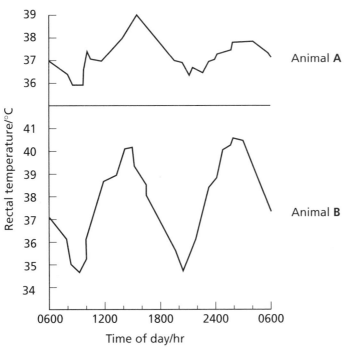

(g) Suggest why there is a smaller daily temperature fluctuation in animal **A** than in animal **B**.

....

....

.... (3)

AEB

3 (a) By reference to the diagram below, briefly explain the principle of dialysis as used in kidney machines.

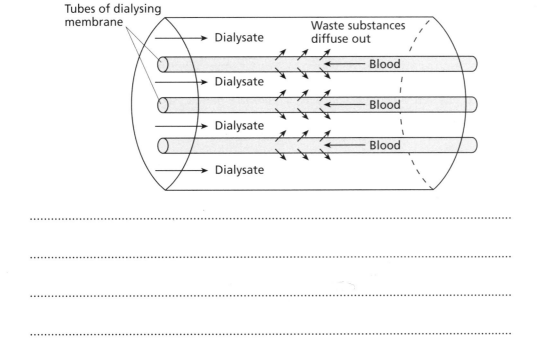

....

....

....

....

.... (6)

(b) State what you think would happen if the glucose concentration of the dialysate were to be a *lower* concentration than that in the patient's blood.

.... (1)

(c) State *two* advantages of providing patients with transplanted kidneys compared with providing them with kidney dialysis machines.

1 ....

2 .... (2)

Oxford

4 (a) Define *osmosis* using the term 'water potential'.

....

.... (2)

(b) Briefly explain *three* reasons why the process of osmosis is important to a herbaceous plant.

(i) ....

.... (2)

(ii) ....

.... (2)

(iii) ....

.... (2)

(c) Cell A and cell B lie adjacent to each other in a plant tissue. The pressure potential (turgor pressure) ψp of cell A is +800 kPa, and that of cell B +600kPa. The solution potential of the vacuolar sap (osmotic potential) for cell A is −1200 kPa and for cell B −1400 kPa.

(i) What is the water potential ($\psi\tau$) of cell A? (Show how you arrive at your answer.)

....

.... (2)

(ii) What is the water potential of ($\psi\tau$) of cell B?

.... (1)

(iii) In which direction might it be said that the water potential gradient is decreasing?

.... (1)

(iv) In which direction is water most likely to move?

.... (1)

(d) (i) Name the type of cell which is responsible for water conduction through the plant.

.... (1)

(ii) State two structural features which enable these cells to perform this function efficiently.

....

.... (2)

Oxford

5 The diagram represents a nephron from a human kidney.

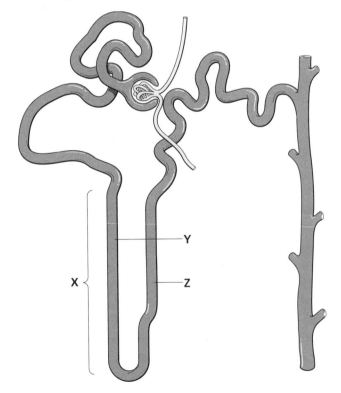

(a) Name the part labelled **X**.

.... (1)

(b) Sodium chloride is actively pumped out of **Z** into the medulla of the kidney. This sodium chloride moves back into **Y**.

Explain the effect of the sodium chloride concentration in the medulla of the kidney on the reabsorption of water from the collecting duct.

.... (1)

(c) Most of the sodium chloride filtered into the glomerular filtrate is reabsorbed.

(i) From which parts of the nephron does this reabsorption take place?

....

.... (2)

(ii) How is the reabsorption of sodium chloride controlled?

....

.... (2)

AEB

6 The graph shows the responses to *two* identical doses of the same antigen.

(a) (i) Identify two differences between the responses shown.

.... (1)

(ii) Briefly explain the mechanism which accounts for these differences.

....

....

.... (3)

(b) How many days after the first injection should the second injection be given? Explain your answer.

.... (1)

AEB

Reproduction and development 6

Animal reproduction

1 There are several methods of **asexual** reproduction in animals. One type is **binary fission**, where the animal splits in half. Another is by **regeneration**, in which missing parts are reformed. A third is by **budding**, where the new organism forms as an outgrowth of the parent and pinches off to become separate.

2 **Sexual** reproduction involves **fertilisation**, which can be **internal** or **external**. In external fertilisation, many gametes are shed outside the body but very few result in offspring.

3 The chances of successful fertilisation are increased if it is internal, and reproduction may be timed to occur when the chances of survival of the offspring are optimal. In mammals, this timing is controlled by the **oestrous cycle**.

4 In women, the **menstrual cycle** begins at **puberty** and continues until **menopause**.

5 During each cycle the **endometrium** becomes engorged with blood, which will provide nutrients and oxygen for the early **embryo**. If fertilisation does not occur, the endometrium is shed, marking the **menstrual period**.

6 At the beginning of the menstrual cycle, two hormones from the pituitary gland – **follicle stimulating hormone (FSH)** and **luteinizing hormone (LH)**, stimulate the development of egg-bearing **follicles** in the **ovaries**. As the follicles mature, they secrete the hormone **oestrogen**, which causes the endometrium to thicken. One follicle usually matures first. LH triggers the release of the egg from this follicle. The **corpus luteum** from the follicle left behind in the ovary secretes the hormones oestrogen and **progesterone**, which cause the endometrium to prepare for a fertilised egg and inhibit the production of FSH, thereby preventing the start of a new cycle. When fertilisation does not occur, the corpus luteum stops its secretions, so the endometrium breaks down and is lost. If fertilisation does occur, the embryo implants in the endometrium and begins to grow, obtaining its requirements from the **placenta**.

7 **Spermatozoa** are propelled towards the egg by using their tails, cilia in the **oviducts** and currents created by vaginal contractions. Fertilisation takes place in the oviduct. Many millions of sperm released die due to natural causes or the unfavourable acidic environment of the female reproductive system. Many are destroyed by the female's white blood cells. Although many sperm may reach the egg, only one effects fertilisation. This is because of changes that take place in the **egg membrane** during initial penetration.

8 The **zygote** travels along the oviduct to the **uterus** and divides by mitosis as it does so. Soon it embeds in the endometrium and begins to obtain nourishment from the mother's blood.

Animal development

1 Fertilisation results in an **embryo**, with all the genetic information it will ever have.

2 When one sperm penetrates an egg it prevents the entry of others. The two sets of chromosomes join, and a series of mitotic divisions, called **cleavage**, divide the embryo into many cells. Cleavage results in a ball of cells called a **morula**. When a cavity called the **blastocoel** forms, the ball is called a **blastocyst**. In **gastrulation**, cells migrate inwards to form a new cavity, the **archenteron**, which opens to the outside through the **blastopore**. Gastrulation forms three **germ layers**, the **ectoderm**, the **mesoderm** and the **endoderm**.

3 Each germ layer develops into specific tissues. Ectoderm forms the outer layers, sense organs and nervous system. Mesoderm forms muscle, bone, cartilage, blood, cardiovascular system, gonads and kidneys. Endoderm contributes largely to the lungs and certain digestive structures.

❹ Cell specialization increases as development proceeeds. Although the developmental fate of cells in some animals is flexible, with few exceptions mammalian cell **differentiation** is permanent. Developmental changes occur in a specific sequence determined by signals that switch sets of genes on or off.

❺ Human development can be divided into three stages. During the first, cleavage begins in the oviduct as the embryo moves towards the uterus. About a week after fertilisation, at the blastocyst stage, the embryo implants in the uterus. At this time the embryo is composed of a thin-walled **trophoblast**, which will form the **embryonic membranes**, and the inner cell mass, which will become the embryo.

❻ The first nutrition of the human embryo is from a mixture of blood and glycogen. After about 12 days **chorionic villi** form. Soon the placenta forms from embryonic and maternal tissues and delivers nutrients from the mother's blood, removes wastes from fetal blood and functions in gas exchange.

❼ During the first stage all major sturctures and organs begin to form. At the end of the second month, the embryo is called a **fetus**. The second stage is marked by rapid growth and the beginning of movement. During the third stage, the fetus grows to fill the available space. Development is completed and the fetus assumes a head-down position.

❽ A series of uterine contractions push the baby through the dilated **cervix** and vagina. The **umbilical cord** is then tied and cut. The placenta is expelled as the **afterbirth**.

Plant reproduction and development

❶ There are disadvantages of sexual reproduction. They include wastage of gametes, gene dilution and possible breeding failure. Recessive genes are masked in the diploid condition, and with the high variability of sexually reproducing populations, this is an advantage, allowing protection from devastation if conditions change.

❷ In lower plants, such as green algae, the haploid **gametophyte generation** is dominant, but in higher plants, the diploid **sporophyte generation** is dominant. In complex green algae, a large, well protected, immobile, energy-rich egg is fertilised by a motile male gamete.

❸ In mosses, a flagellated male gamete swims from an **antheridium** to an egg, which is held in a flask-shaped **archegonium**. The diploid zygote develops into a sporophyte, which produces spores by meiosis. The spores germinate to form haploid gametophytes, which will have either archegonia or antheridia.

❹ The gametophytes of ferns lack water-conducting tissue and are very small. Male gametes (**antherozooids**) swim through a film of water to reach the egg in the archegonium. The sporophyte is dominant.

❺ In cone-bearing plants, like pine trees, a **microspore mother cell** in a male pine cone undergoes meiosis to produce **pollen grains**, each composed of two cells, a protective coat and wing-like extensions that carry the pollen on the wind. When it lands on a female cone, pollen germinates, producing a **pollen tube** that reaches the female archegonium. In female pine cones, **megaspore mother cells** undergo meiosis, each producing four cells. One of these will develop into a female gametophyte, with many nuclei in the cytoplasm. One of these nuclei, the egg nucleus, is fertilised by a male gamete nucleus from a pollen grain.

❻ A generalised flower is made of four whorls of modified leaves arising from the **receptacle**. The **calyx** is formed from leaf-like **sepals**, which protect the developing **bud**. The **corolla** is made of **petals**, which may attract insects for **pollination**. The **stamens** consist of **filaments** and **anthers** and are the male reproductive organs. The **carpels** are the female reproductive organs and consist of the **stigma**, **style** and **ovary**. The male gametophyte is produced in the **anther** and is released as **pollen**. The female gametophyte is produced in the ovary of the carpel. This will house the developing embryos inside the **seed**s and will finally form the **fruit**.

7 Each **ovule** in the ovary consists of a megaspore mother cell and nutritive or protective tissues. The diploid megaspore mother cell undergoes meiosis to produce four haploid cells. Only one survives as a functional megaspore cell and it divides mitotically to form a female gametophyte, now called the **embryo sac**, which contains eight haploid nuclei in seven cells. The two nuclei sharing a cell are called the **polar nuclei**. The egg forms from one of three haploid nuclei in cells isolated at one end of the ovary.

8 Each of the diploid microspore mother cells in the pollen sacs of the anther undergoes meiosis, producing four haploid microspores. Each microspore divides mitotically and produces the male gametophyte (pollen grain), which consists of a 'sperm' cell and a pollen tube cell with a protective coat.

9 When the pollen grain lands on the stigma pollination occurs. The pollen grain sends a pollen tube down the style. The pollen tube nucleus is near the tip of the tube and the **generative nucleus**, which divides to produce two 'sperm' enters the embryo sac. One 'sperm', fertilises the egg and forms the zygote. The other fuses with the two polar nuclei and forms a nutritive tissue (**endosperm**). The embryo develops one or more **cotyledons** that serve as an immediate source of food.

10 The embryo develops inside the seed, where it is protected by a tough seed coat until suitable conditions trigger germination. The seed develops in the ovary, which divides by mitosis to form the fruit.

11 Plant development differs from animal development because plants must grow by adding cells to the periphery and do not stop growing.

12 Before a seed germinates, the endosperm nucleus divides. Then the zygote divides and forms a small cell that divides again to produce a stalk of cells. The end of the stalk divides to form the embryo. Cell differentiation within the embryo produces cells that will become **epidermis**, **vascular tissue** and **cortex**.

13 The embryo elongates and forms embryonic leaves called cotyledons.

14 Some plant tissues (**meristems**) remain in an undifferentiated condition. The **apical** meristem is responsible for growth in length of roots and stems. The **lateral** meristem (**cambium**) allows for growth in diameter.

15 Other specialised tissues include the thick-walled supporting tissues, **sclerenchyma** and **collenchyma**, and the thin-walled **parenchyma** cells, which contain many vacuoles and, in some, chloroplasts.

16 Hormones are substances produced in one part, of an organism and are transported to another part where they exert their effects. Three plant hormones involved in growth and development are **auxins**, **giberellins** and **cytokinins**. Auxins cause cell elongation, which enables plants to grow towards light. Giberellins increase the stem length by stimulating cell division and cell elongation. Giberellins also stimulate pollen germination, the growth of pollen tubes in certain plants and break **dormancy** of many kinds of seeds. Cytokinins increase growth of plant embryos or plant cells in tissue culture and react with auxin to cause rapid cell division. Cytokinin enhances seed germination once it has started and prevents leaves from turning yellow.

If you need to revise this subject more thoroughly, see the relevant topics in the *Letts* A level *Biology Study Guide*.

1 The graph shows the concentrations of the hormones progesterone and human chorionic gonadotrophin (HCG) in the blood during the early stages of a human pregnancy.

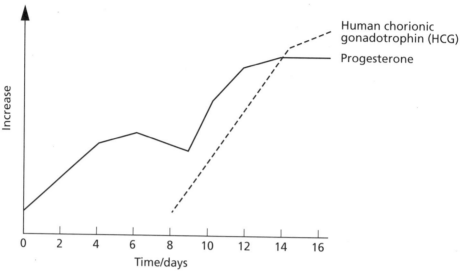

(a) Describe how the progesterone curve would differ if pregnancy had not occurred.

....

.... (2)

(b) Name the site of secretion of progesterone during:

(i) the period shown in the graph;

.... (1)

(ii) the last 3 months of the pregnancy.

.... (1)

(c) (i) Suggest the main function of human chorionic gonadotrophin in early pregnancy.

....

.... (1)

(ii) Give evidence from the graph to support your answer to (c)(i).

....

.... (1)

AEB

2 The diagram shows a section through the ovary and pollen tube of a flowering plant just before fertilisation.

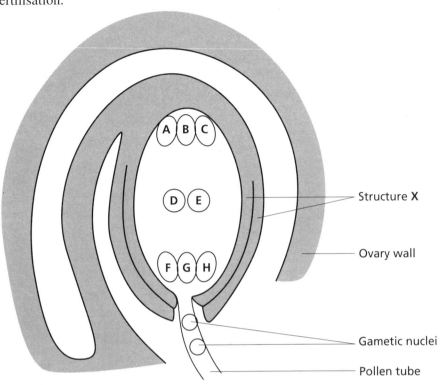

(a) Which of the nuclei labelled **A** to **H** fuse with a gametic nucleus to form:

 (i) the endosperm;

 .... (1)

 (ii) the zygote?

 .... (1)

(b) After fertilisation, into what structure does each of the following develop:

 (i) the ovary wall;

 .... (1)

 (ii) the structure labelled **X**?

 .... (1)

(c) In this plant, the diploid number of chromosomes is 14. How many chromosomes would you expect to find in:

 (i) the nucleus labelled **C**;

 .... (1)

(ii) a nucleus in the endosperm?

.... (1)

AEB

3 The photograph is an electron micrograph of a section through part of a human placenta.

(a) What type of blood vessel is **A**? Give a reason for your answer.

....

.... (2)

(b) (i) Explain why the red blood cells shown in the photograph are of different size and shape.

....

.... (2)

(ii) Why do the red blood cells appear dark in colour?

.... (1)

(iii) Explain why the red blood cells appear uniformly dark while the nuclei have patches of darker and lighter colour.

....

....

.... (3)

(c) Explain why an electron micrograph does not always accurately represent an actual tissue.

....

.... (2)

(d) (i) Describe and explain how *two* features visible in the photograph contribute to the efficient diffusion of oxygen from maternal to fetal blood.

....

....

.... (4)

Magnified part of copper grid — Blood vessel A — Fetal red blood cells — Maternal blood — Magnified part of copper grid

(ii) Describe how the characteristics of fetal haemoglobin enable it to transport oxygen from the placenta to the cells of the fetus.

....

....

.... (3)

(e) (i) Name *two* substances where the net movement is in the direction of the arrow.

.... (1)

(ii) Describe *one* function of the placenta other than its involvement in the passage of substances between mother and fetus.

....

.... (2)

AEB

4   An investigation was carried out into the relationship between the birth mass of human babies and concentrations of lead and zinc in the mother's placenta. The results are shown in the histogram below. Each bar represents the mean of many measurements.

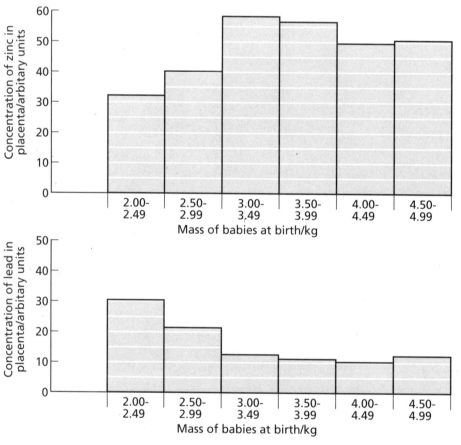

(a) Describe the relationship between (i) placental lead and birth mass and (ii) placental zinc and birth mass. Suggest an explanation for each relationship.

(i) Lead

....

....

.... (3)

(ii) Zinc

....

....

.... (3)

(b) Suggest how metal ions such as lead and zinc might pass from the environment to the placenta.

....

.... (2)

(c) State *three* other factors that can affect the birth mass of human babies.

1 ....

2 ....

3 .... (3)

ULEAC

5 (a) The graph shows the change in the mean diameter of follicles and corpora lutea in the ovary of a pig.

Ref: Hammond's Farm Animals by Hammond, Bowman and Robinson (1983)

(i) Name the hormone which stimulates the follicle to start development at point **X**.

.... (1)

(ii) Describe the evidence for ovulation in the graph.

.... (1)

(iii) Use the graph to estimate the length of the oestrous cycle in the pig.

.... (1)

(iv) Pregnancy did not occur in the period of time shown on the graph. Describe *two* ways in which the graph would differ if pregnancy had occurred during the first cycle.

1 ....

2 .... (2)

(b) The diagrams show stages in the process of implantation in a Mammal.

Endothelium

Uterine epithelium

Structure **A**

(i) Name Structure **A**.

.... (1)

(ii) Give *one* reason why implantation is necessary if **A** is to complete development.

.... (1)

(c) Fetal and maternal blood never come into direct contact in the placenta. Suggest two advantages of this to the fetus.

1 ....

2 .... (2)

(d) The procedure called chorionic villus sampling allows some inherited diseases to be diagnosed early in pregnancy. A syringe is used to suck up connective tissue cells of the chorion which form part of the placenta.

Suggest why these cells

(i) are of the same genotype as the fetus.

.... (1)

(ii) contain chromosomes which are clearly visible under a microscope.

.... (1)

WJEC

6 In some women infertility may be treated with the drug clomiphene. The graph shows the blood-oestrogen levels in a woman during and after treatment with clomiphene.

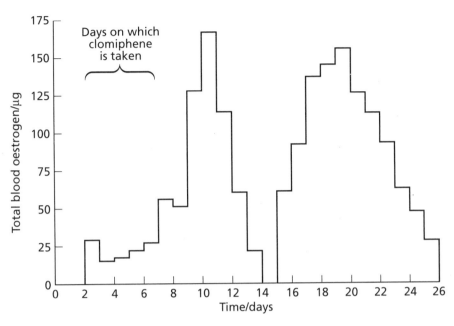

(a) Clomiphene stimulates the production of gonadotrophic hormones from the anterior pituitary gland.

   (i) From the timing of the treatment shown in the graph, name the gonadotrophic hormone whose secretion is stimulated by the clomiphene.

   .... (1)

   (ii) Explain how stimulation of this hormone brings about the change in oestrogen secretion shown in the graph.

   ....

   .... (2)

(b) (i) On what day would ovulation be most likely to occur?

   .... (1)

   (ii) Give a reason for your answer.

   .... (1)

   AEB

7 Inheritance and selection

REVISION
SUMMARY

Genetics

❶ The principle of dominance, formulated by Gregor Mendel, states that a **dominant** character is one of a pair of contrasted characters, which shows itself in a **heterozygote** (hybrid). A **recessive** character only shows itself in a **homozygote**.

❷ Mendel's **principle of segregation** states that 'of a pair of contrasted characters only one can be present in a gamete and is represented by a germinal unit (**gene**)'. So, when two hybrids mate, statistically, they will produce a ratio of three offspring showing the dominant character to one showing the recessive character.

❸ A heterozygote is an individual receiving unlike **alleles** from both parents.
A homozygote is an individual receiving similar alleles from both parents.

❹ Mendel's **principle of independent assortment** states that 'either of a pair of alleles can combine with any of another pair'.

❺ In order to test whether an individual is heterozygous or homozygous for a dominant character, a **test cross** can be carried out, in which a recessive individual is crossed with the dominant one. If any recessive offspring result, the dominant parent must have been heterozygous.

❻ Many of Mendel's observations can be related to the behaviour of chromosomes during meiosis.

❼ The sex of an individual is determined by a pair of **sex chromosomes**. Those chromosomes that are responsible for characteristics other than sex determination are called **autosomes**. In mammals and most insects the male sex chromosomes are X and Y, and those of females are X and X. When sperms are produced, the X and Y chromosomes pair and separate, so that half the sperms carry an X and half carry a Y. Since females are XX, all eggs must carry an X chromosome.

❽ The X chromosome carries some genes not concerned with sex determination. In the fruit fly *Drosophila*, a gene for eye colour is on the X chromosome, and in humans the X chromosome may have an allele for colour blindness, or haemophilia.
Recessive alleles on the X chromosome will be expressed in males because they lack the dominant counterpart on the Y chromosome, but will only be expressed in females who are homozygous recessive for the trait.

❾ Cells of women have dark specks called **Barr bodies**, and the nucleus of a white bood cell in women may have a structure called a **drumstick**. Both are thought to be inactive X chromosomes. Barr bodies and drumsticks are not found in the cells of men.

❿ Abnormal development of sexual characteristics may result from an imbalance of sex chromosomes. **Turner's syndrome** results from a female having only one X chromosome in each of her cells. **Kleinfelter's syndrome** occurs in XXY males.

⓫ **Linkage** of genes can occur between two or more genes on the same chromosome. Linked genes will be inherited together unless **crossing over** occurs between them during meiosis.

⓬ **Gene maps** showing the positions of genes on chromosomes can be made by using the information from the observations of cross overs. The percentage cross over is proportional to the distance between two genes on a chromosome.

⓭ **Mutation** is a change in genetic material. It can be caused by X-rays, certain chemicals, and ultra-violet radiation. Mutations that alter a gene (**gene** or **point mutation**) occur when a nucleotide is omitted or repeated, or the wrong one added during DNA replication. Mutations involving the structure or number of chromosomes (**chromosomal mutations**) may involve **deletions**, **inversions** or **duplications**.

⑭ There are several reasons why the 3 : 1 ratio in the appearance of a characteristic may not result from a cross between parents differing in the expression of the characteristic. Some alleles show **incomplete dominance** and produce intermediate effects. Some genes have **multiple** (three or more) **alleles**.

In **epistasis**, one gene masks the expression of a gene at another **locus**. For example, in mice the gene for albinism masks the expression of the gene determining coat colour. In **polygenic inheritance**, different genes have an additive effect on a characteristic, producing variation in expression. Variation in gene expression may be caused by factors including environmental conditions, gender and age.

⑮ A population is a group of interbreeding individuals. The **frequency** of alleles for any characteristic will remain unchanged in a population through all generations unless it is altered by an external factor, such as better survival and reproduction by those individuals bearing a particular allele, non-random mating, mutation or accidents affecting a small population. **Evolution** is a change in gene ratios (gene frequencies).

Applied genetics

❶ Specific genes can be removed from chromosomes and then inserted into chromosomes of other species. These will then duplicate the gene as they reproduce and will have the potential to produce large amounts of the gene product for human use.

❷ When DNA containing a useful gene is inserted into the DNA of another species, the result is called **recombinant DNA**.

❸ In order to produce recombinant DNA, chromosomes containing the wanted gene are broken into fragments. **Restriction enzymes** cut DNA at specific parts, leaving uneven ends called **sticky ends** because their unpaired bases can join with other fragments having complementary sequences of nucleotides.

❹ Each piece of chromosome is inserted into a host chromosome of a different cell. The cell that produces the gene product contains a DNA fragment with the wanted gene. The fragments are transferred to bacterial cells where many exact copies can be made by cloning. A **clone** is a group of identical organisms with a single common ancestor.

❺ The transfer needs a **vector**, which is an organism used to transfer the source DNA to the host DNA. Common vectors are bacteria that contain circular chromosomes together with a small circle of DNA called a **plasmid**. DNA fragments are spliced into plasmids using restriction enzymes. The plasmids carry the inserted DNA to new host bacterial cells for cloning. Since plasmids also contain genes for resistance to antibiotics, plasmid-containing cells are selected by exposing all cells to antibiotics.

❻ The cells containing the useful gene are identified by screening for the gene product or by matching up the base sequence in the DNA.

❼ This form of **genetic engineering** has many practical applications. It has been used to make large amounts of proteins, such as insulin and other hormones. It has the potential for making plants resistant to diseases and pests, and even to allow them to accept nitrogen-fixing bacteria from leguminous plants.

Certain human metabolic disorders, such as Alzheimer's disease and Huntington's chorea might be diagnosed by detection of genes.

The process of selection

❶ One definition of evolution is 'the change in a population through time'. The combination of Charles Darwin's ideas and Mendelian genetics is called **Neo-Darwinism**.

❷ A **species** is a population whose members can interbreed to produce fertile offspring. There are at least two problems with this concept of a species. One is determining whether individuals without the opportunity to mate could actually do so. The other is deciding whether individuals at the extremes of a range, who are unable to successfully interbreed, are of the same species when subgroups interbreed all along the range.

❸ **Reproductive isolation** takes place when one group is unable to interbreed with another. This takes place due to geographical barriers; behavioural differences, such as mating signals; differences in the anatomy of reproductive systems; differences in genes that prevent pairing and embryological development; or the production of sterile hybrid offspring.

❹ The formation of a new species is called **speciation**. **Allopatric speciation** is most common in animals in which subgroups become isolated from the parent group. When this occurs, genetic differences accumulate within each group and prevent interbreeding if the groups become rejoined.

❺ The formation of new species from groups living in the same area is called **sympatric speciation**, and is most common in plants. It may occur by **hybridization**, especially in flowering plants. **Polyploidy** can also give rise to new plant species. Here, doubling or quadrupling of sets of chromosomes takes place, as a mutation when chromosomes fail to separate during mitosis.

❻ Differences between species living in different environments are increased by **divergent evolution**. In contrast, **convergent evolution** increases the similarities of species living in similar environments.

❼ If the environment changes, **variation** will be of an advantage because it increases the chances of survival for breeding and produces offspring that survive under new conditions.

❽ Variation is the prerequiste for evolution by **natural selection**. The best adapted individuals leave the most offspring.

❾ Variation in a character such as height in humans can be expressed graphically. It will produce a bell-shaped curve. Individuals with extreme forms of the characteristic will be eliminated by high selection pressure. More individuals with extreme characteristcs may survive if the selection pressure is low and therefore the base of the curve is wider.

❿ When the environment is stable, **stabilizing selection** results in a population clustered around an average condition, and may be assumed to be optimal for the existing conditions. When environmental conditions change, **directional selection** results in changes in the population as the population conforms to the new conditions.

If you need to revise this subject more thoroughly, see the relevant topics in the *Letts* A level *Biology Study Guide*.

⓫ An example of selection is the change in the frequency of light- and dark-coloured moths in a population that occurred during the industrial revolution (**industrial melanism**). Before the industrial revolution, light moths were more common because they were concealed on the lichen-covered tree bark, while dark moths were easily seen by predators. As the trees became darkened with soot made by burning fossil fuel, the number of dark moths increased because they were now camouflaged. The light moths were now more conspicuous and were eaten by predators.

⓬ Small populations may evolve by **genetic drift** when chance causes a change in gene frequency. If a population is suddenly reduced in size, the gene frequencies of the survivors may not be representative of the original population. Gene frequencies of small populations may also be changed through the **founder effect**, in which a few organisms become separated from the main population and establish their own breeding group. The gene frequencies of the new group changes further in response to selection pressure in the new environment.

⓭ Small populations may easily become extinct because they lack a sufficiently large **gene pool**, and genes that are a disadvantage to breeding may accumulate.

1 Red-green colour blindness is an inherited condition which causes affected individuals to confuse the colours red and green.

The table shows the approximate percentage of red-green colour blindness in different populations.

Population	Sample size	% colour blind	
		Male	Female
Arabs	337	10.0	1.00
Swiss	2000	8.0	0.64
British	16,180	6.6	0.36
Japanese	259,000	4.0	0.16
Eskimos	297	2.5	0.06
Fiji Islanders	608	0.8	0.006

Ref: Adapted from Human Biology by Harrison, Weiner, Tanner and Barnicot (1982)

(a) (i) State *two* general conclusions which can be drawn from the data. Suggest an explanation for each

1 Conclusion ....

....

Explanation ....

....

....

2 Conclusion ....

....

Explanation ....

....

.... (4)

(b) (i) Suggest the name given to the way in which colour blindness is transmitted.

.... (1)

(ii) The table suggests that about 0.4% of women in Britain are red-green colour blind. Use appropriate symbols to complete the genetic diagram to show the most likely way in which this defect arises in women.

	Male	Female
Parental phenotype:	....	....
Parental genotype:	....	....

Gametes: ◯   ◯   ◯   ◯

Offspring genotypes: ....

Offspring phenotypes: ....

....   (5)

WJEC

2 In some genetic engineering processes a synthetic gene is inserted into a bacterial host. This process is shown in the diagram below.

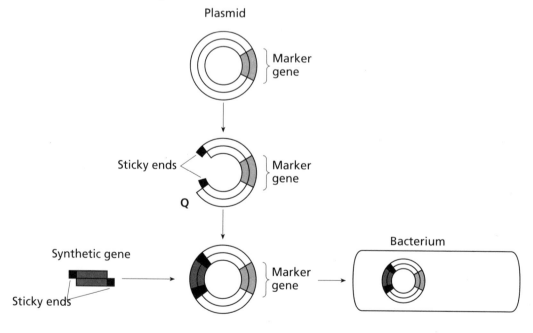

(a) (i) What term is used to describe the function of the plasmid in this process?

.... (1)

(ii) Name the type of enzyme used at Q to cleave (cut) the DNA.

.... (1)

(b) Genetically engineered human insulin is now used in the treatment of diabetes. State *three* advantages of the use of this type of insulin.

1 ....

....

2 ....

....

3 ....

.... (3)

ULEAC

3 The typical form of the European Swallow-tail butterfly has yellow patches on its wings, but in a rare variety called *nigra* these areas are shaded black.

A cross between a typical male and a *nigra* female produced 14 typical offspring and 6 *nigra*.

(a) As a first hypothesis to explain this result, it was suggested that the *nigra* variety is caused by a recessive allele of a single gene which is not sex-linked.

(i) On the basis of this hypothesis, a 1:1 ratio would be expected in the offspring.

Construct a genetic diagram to show the genotypes of the parents of this cross, and to show how this ratio could be obtained.

Use the letters **N** and **n** to represent the two alleles of the gene.

(3)

(ii) The table below gives the expected numbers (E) of each phenotype on the basis of this hypothesis, and the differences between the observed and expected numbers ($O - E$).

Phenotype	Observed number	Expected number	Difference
	O	E	$O - E$
Typical	14	10	4
Nigra	6	10	−4

Using the formula below, calculate the value of chi-squared (χ^2). Show your working.

$$\chi^2 = \Sigma \ \frac{(O - E)^2}{E}$$

Answer χ^2 = ... (3)

(iii) Probability levels (P) corresponding to some values of χ^2 in this case are shown below.

χ^2	0.004	2.71	3.85	6.63
$P(\%)$	95	10	5	1

What does your calculated value for χ^2 indicate in relation to this particular cross?

....

.... (1)

(b) A second hypothesis was suggested, in which the *nigra* variety is produced by interaction between two unlinked genes, **A** and **B**. One of the other genes has alleles **A** and **a** and the other gene has alleles **B** and **b**. The *nigra* phenotype is seen only in individuals which are homozygous for the **a** allele and *either* homozygous *or* heterozygous for the **B** allele (*either* **aaBB** *or* **aaBb**).

This second hypothesis suggested that the genotypes of the original parents in the above cross were as follows.

The typical parent   **AaBb**

The *nigra* parent   **aaBb**

Construct a genetic diagram to show the genotype and phenotype ratios expected from this cross on the basis of the second hypothesis.

(4)

(c) Comparison of the observed results with those expected from the second hypothesis gives a value for χ^2 of 0.48.

Compare this with the value calculated for the first hypothesis and suggest which hypothesis has the greater probability of being correct. Justify your answer.

....

....

....

.... (2)

ULEAC

4 Cells of the bacterium *E. coli* were grown for many generations on a medium containing the heavy isotope of nitrogen, ^{15}N. This labelled all the DNA in the bacteria.

The cells were transferred to a medium containing ^{14}N and allowed to grow. During each generation of bacteria, the DNA replicates once. Samples of the bacteria were removed from the culture after one generation time and after two generation times. The DNA from each sample was extracted and centrifuged. As the DNA containing ^{15}N is slightly heavier than that containing ^{14}N, the relative amounts of DNA labelled with ^{14}N and ^{15}N can be determined.

The diagram shows two reference tubes and the results of this experiment.

Reference tubes			Results of experiment	
Specimen of DNA with ^{14}N	Specimen of DNA with ^{15}N	DNA from cells grown in ^{15}N	DNA from cells after one generation in ^{14}N	DNA from cells after two generations in ^{14}N

Tube **X**

(a) Which part of the DNA molecule in the original culture would have been labelled with ^{15}N?

.... (1)

(b) Explain why the DNA occupies an intermediate position after one generation in the ^{14}N–containing medium.

....

.... (2)

(c) Complete the diagram to show the position of the band or bands of DNA after two generations in the ^{14}N-containing medium (Tube **X**).   (1)

AEB

5 (a) Give *one* reason for the extensive use of *Drosophila* in breeding experiments.

.... (1)

(b) In *Drosophila*, the separate alleles controlling the traits for vestigial wings and for gouty legs are recessive to wild type; gouty legs are short and thick.

A cross of the following phenotypes was made:

Phenotype **A**   Phenotype **B**
wild type wings : wild type legs × wild type wings : gouty legs

The following progeny were obtained:

26	wild type wings	:	wild type legs
20	wild type wings	:	gouty legs
5	vestigial wings	:	wild type legs
10	vestigial wings	:	gouty legs

Using the symbols **V** and **G** to represent the wild type alleles, complete the table below to show the genotypes of the parents with respect to wings and legs.

	Phenotype A	Phenotype B
Wings		
Legs		

(c) Haemophilia is a trait determined by a sex-linked recessive gene carried on the X chromosome.

Queen Victoria was heterozygous for the haemophilia gene; Prince Albert, her husband, was not affected.

Their family is shown in the following diagram.

Queen Victoria ⊙——————————□ Prince Albert

○ □ ⊙   □ □ ■ ⊙

□ normal male

■ haemophiliac male

○ normal female

⊙ female carrier

(i) For the family tree given above, state the genotypes of

Queen Victoria ....

Prince Albert .... (1)

(ii) Theoretically, what percentage of their sons would be expected to have inherited the trait haemophilia?

.... (1)

(d) Hairy ears is a trait which is transmitted from a father who has this condition to his sons; it never occurs in girls.

Suggest a hypothesis to explain this inheritance pattern.

.... (1)

(e) How does the karyotype of an individual with Down's Syndrome differ from that of a normal individual?

.... (1)

SEB

6 The enzyme β-galactosidase breaks down the sugar lactose.

The bacterium *Escherischia coli* produces β-galactosidase only when lactose is available. The diagram below represents the section of DNA which controls the synthesis of β-galactosidase.

Regulator gene   Operator gene   Structural gene

| R | | O | S | |

Repressor molecule

| P |

(a) Draw an arrow from box P to show the new position of the repressor molecule if lactose is *not* present. (1)

QUESTIONS

(b) Explain why no β-galactosidase is synthesised when P is in that position.

.... (1)

(c) Explain how the presence of lactose molecules induces the production of β-galactosidase.

....

.... (2)

(d) What is the advantage of this control mechanism to *E. coli*?

.... (1)

SEB

Biomes and communities

❶ **Ecology** is the study of the interrelations of organisms between and within **environments**. A **habitat** is the place where an organism lives. The organism's requirements and the ways in which it interacts with both the living and non-living components of its environment make up its **niche**.

❷ Two species cannot occupy the same niche indefinitely. If two species co-exist, it is assumed that they are occupying different niches. Partitioning a habitat reduces the level of **competition**. Competition occurs when two organisms use scarce resources or harm each other when seeking the same resource.

❸ The Earth's terrestrial **biosphere** can be divided into several kinds of region called **biomes**, which are defined according to the plants they support. The nature of the plant community is dependent on factors such as soil conditions, climate, competition, as well as the abundance of herbivores and their predators. The nature of the plant **community** influences the kinds of animal that inhabit the biome. Six biomes exist: temperate deciduous forest, grasslands, deserts, tropical rain forest, tundra and taiga.

❹ The dominant trees in the **temperate deciduous forest** are oak, beech, poplar and maple. These all shed their leaves in winter and grow rapidly in summer.
   Many annuals appear in the spring before the new tree leaves shade the forest floor. The annual rainfall is 75 cm – 125 cm.

❺ **Grasslands** are characterised by many species of grass, shrub and bush. In some parts of the world bamboo will make up the grass component. Annual rainfall is 25 cm – 100 cm.

❻ **Deserts** have hot days and cold nights. Annual rainfall is less than 25 cm per year. Plants are adapted to grow and reproduce at times when water becomes available. They store water and have deep tap roots to reach underground sources. Many plants are **xerophytes**, which are modified to reduce water loss from leaves and stems.

❼ **Tropical rain forests** experience a constant temperature and heavy rainfall. Some have rainy seasons. There is a rich variety of organisms. Competition is keen. Trees grow to great heights and form canopies where their branches meet. Where sun filters through the canopy, **jungles** form. Rainfall is between 200 cm – 400 cm per year.

❽ Both the **arctic tundra** in the far north and the **alpine tundra** at high altitude have a covering of ice and snow, except during the short 2 – 4 month summer, when the soil above the **permafrost** becomes boggy and ponds form. Lichens, mosses, grassses and a few trees are found. The variety of large mammals is limited and recovery from disturbance is low.

❾ The **taiga**, or coniferous forest of the north, has long cold and wet winters with short summer growing seasons. Large bogs are common. Due to a carpet of pine needles, few plants can survive.

❿ Because they are small, bodies of freshwater are less stable than seawater. One of the signs of ageing, **eutrophication**, is speeded up when human activity adds nitrates and phosphates from fertilisers and detergents to bodies of freshwater. With the extra mineral nutrients provided in this way, plants flourish. When they die, they decay and bacteria deplete oxygen.

⓫ The oceans cover three quarters of the Earth's surface and have an average depth of 5 km. Due to surface winds, the deep water is in constant motion. Upwelling, which occurs where currents are deflected upwards by undersea mountains, brings nutrients from the sediments upwards to stimulate the growth of **phytoplankton**. The phytoplankton are important as **producers** in food chains.

⓬ A community includes only the living organisms, whereas the **ecosystem** includes all the interacting living and non-living components that form an independent unit.

⓭ Ecosystems with complex **food webs** are more stable than those with simple ones. **Extinction** simplifies ecosystems.

Population dynamics

1 The population size of some species is more or less constant. Others are decreasing or increasing in numbers. Reasons for concern over the numbers of species becoming extinct include the loss of a product that may be of use and the ethical point that species other than mankind have a right to exist.

2 The unrestricted reproductive capacity of a population is its **biotic potential**. Organisms living in an environment with unlimited resources have a rapid rate of increase, which is described by a J-shaped growth curve.

3 A population rarely reaches its full biotic potential due to **environmental resistance**, which includes those environmental factors that reduce a population's increase. As a population reaches the **carrying capacity** of the environment, environmental resistance increases and growth slows. This type of growth is described by an S-shaped growth curve.

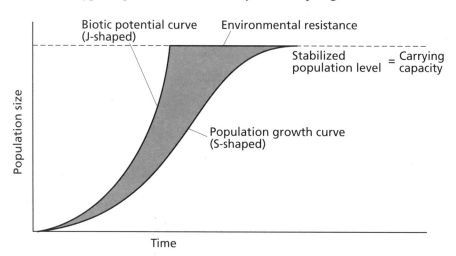

4 If a population greatly exceeds its carrying capacity, the environmental overuse may cause the population numbers to fall drastically. Populations of some species, such as annual plants and insects, undergo regular cycles of **surges** and **crashes**. Some crashes are followed by recovery. Others are more permanent.

5 A way that population growth is regulated is by reproductive rate. Although biotic potential varies among species, it is always very high. One factor determining the reproductive rate is the energy available to the species.

6 Natural selection sets a reproductive strategy in accordance with a species' environment and evolutionary history, so that reproductive success is maximised. In an organism such as an internal **parasite**, in which an individual's success depends on chance, a common reproductive strategy is to produce vast numbers of offspring, but invest little in each. In contrast, mammals, in which an individual's success is increased by protection and learning from parents, produce few young but invest a great deal of time and energy in each one.

7 Population size may be reduced by death. Because **abiotic** factors, such as climate or environmental poisons, are not influenced by the number of individuals in the population, their effects are **density-independent**. **Biotic** population controls such as predation, parasitism, competition and disease are likely to depend on the density of the population (**density-dependence**) and tend to stabilise population size. Predators do not usually wipe out their prey, because a drop in prey is followed by a decrease in predators. A well adapted parasite derives benefit from and harms its **host** without actually killing it. The population-regulating effects of competition can be seen in **territoriality**. An individual that successfully defends a territory is more likely to survive and reproduce than is the loser because the defended area holds nest sites, hiding places or food. The effects of disease are density-dependent because disease spreads more easily at higher population densities and because greater numbers of individuals in a population provide more potential reservoirs of mutant strains of **pathogens**.

Effects of humans on the environment.

1 Meeting the demands of affluent societies generates an enormous amount of waste. **Pollution** is a side effect of this process.

2 A **pollutant** is a harmful substance that enters the environment. Although some is natural, pollution from human activity is of universal concern.

3 Pollutants are harmful in one or more of four possible ways:

- by altering critical aspects of the environment in ways that lead to the destruction of some forms of life;
- by setting the stage for future effects;
- by acting with other pollutants to provide combined effects.

4 Burning fuel is a source of air pollution. Although air pollution occurs everywhere, it is greatest in the cities of industrialised countries. A common air pollutant, carbon monoxide, competes with oxygen for haemoglobin and therefore reduces the capacity for blood to carry oxygen.

Nitrogen dioxide irritates lungs, withers plants and combines with hydrocarbons in the presence of sunlight to produce destructive **photochemical smog**. Arguably, the most dangerous air pollutant is sulphur dioxide, which comes from burning coal and which can react with water to form the sulphuric acid of **acid rain**. Acid rain causes damage to plants and aquatic life. It can dissolve marble and corrode iron and steel. Carbon dioxide is a product of combustion and its build-up in the atmosphere is a likely cause of **global warming**.

5 Much of our fresh water is polluted. It is used for cooling, cleaning and the dumping of industrial and domestic waste. Drinking water in developed countries is filtered and treated with chlorine to kill micro-organisms. If water is contaminated with human waste it may contain the virus responsible for infectious hepatitis. Drinking water may contain thousands of types of industrial chemicals, many with unknown side-effects. When water is used as a coolant it absorbs heat. It it is returned to its source at a higher temperature, it may alter the composition of communities within an ecosystem by lowering the amount of available oxygen or by increasing the concentration of pollutants, as a result of evaporation.

6 Some **pesticides** still contain **D.D.T.** Since World War II, pesticides have drastically reduced the occurrence of insect-borne diseases, but D.D.T.s widespread use has led to the evolution of resistant strains of insects. It also kills beneficial insects. Some pesticides are persistant and accumulate in food chains, reaching toxic levels in top predators.

7 Natural **radiation** may occur from radioactive rocks or in the form of cosmic rays. Humans produce more through medical radiation, nuclear reactors and nuclear accidents. Nuclear power stations could possibly supply much of the needed energy for industrialised countries, but the problem of safe disposal of radioactive waste is as yet unsolved.

REVISION SUMMARY

If you need to revise this subject more thoroughly, see the relevant topics in the *Letts* A level *Biology Study Guide*.

1   Read the following passage carefully and then answer the questions which follow.

Always ready to douse the countryside in chemicals, killing off any plant or animal that cannot be sold for profit, the British farmer is the natural enemy of anyone with a feeling for wildlife. That, at least, is the stereotype, but it could be ready for a change. Faced with the challenge of falling cereal prices, farmers are seldom more ready to consider replacing
5   expensive chemicals with the natural enemies of the pests.

In the short term, chemical sprays are clearly an effective way to control pests like aphids which infest the leaves of cereal plants and can reduce their yield. But sprays are expensive, costing up to £20 per hectare each time they are used, usually two or three times a year. Furthermore, 'broad-spectrum' compounds do harm as well as good; they may be even more
10   effective against beneficial predators than they are against their crop-destroying prey, cause environmental damage and can lead to the evolution of the resistant populations of the insects that they are meant to kill.

Instead of killing pests and their predators indiscriminately, farmers can make the most of species that prey on pests and so reduce the need for spraying. The problem lies in
15   pinpointing the most important species and then managing the farmland to meet their differing needs. Predators fall into two main categories. First there are aphid-specific insects such as hoverflies, ladybirds and parasitoid wasps which are parasitic as larvae and free-living as adults. The other group includes species such as spiders, rove beetles and ground beetles which eat a variety of prey. Farmers keen to employ nature to tend their fields can
20   use two approaches to encourage such creatures. The first is to help them to survive the cold winter months while the second is to augment the food sources in early spring when many predators need sources of protein and energy such as pollen and nectar.

In one study the characteristics of hedges and other field boundaries which help predators to survive over winter were identified. Though hedgebanks are slightly higher, warmer and
25   drier than open fields, these properties alone do not provide sufficient protection. Instead, a key element is the proliferation of tussock-forming grasses. When hedgebanks are sprayed with herbicides, highly competitive weed species take over. Their physical structure, unlike that of tussock-forming species offers little protection for overwintering predators. Further studies demonstrate that in tussocks, temperature vary much less than on bare soil or in the
30   crop itself, although the averages are similar. Coddled by this benign microclimate, predators proliferate and may be as high as 1000 per square metre. In the spring, these predators leave the banks and invade the crop. Careful construction of such banks in the centres of fields thus provides a boon for wingless predators allowing them a high population and placing them close to high concentrations of prey.

35   For farmers this scheme is a valuable one. The research showed that the banks could save 15% of the crop that might otherwise be affected by aphids and this could represent an overall saving of £150 per hectare. Another study concentrated on the predators' needs in spring. It was noted that hoverflies, which can become so effective in controlling aphids that spraying becomes virtually unnecessary, have a particularly great need for pollen and nectar.
40   One reason for their efficiency is that they lay eggs in areas where their aphid prey is scarce. Because they outnumber their prey, a relatively small population of hoverflies will effectively prevent aphid outbreak but females will not lay eggs unless they have consumed enough pollen first.

So how can farmers help? Hoverflies thrive on farms rich in wild flowers, especially
45   those whose open structure gives easy access to pollen and nectar. Such flowers tend to grow in hedge bottoms where they are vulnerable to the effects of carelessly applied herbicides. Attracting the hoverflies, then, is a matter of enriching field boundaries. There are three main ways of doing this: sowing the appropriate native wild flowers along the field margin;

keeping part of the field free from herbicides to let flowering weeds grow within the crop
50 and sowing seeds of non-native flowers such as the American oil radish.

Although methods of encouraging pests' predators on farmland are already showing their worth, there is no point in using them if farmers persist in carelessly spraying broad-spectrum pesticides on the adjacent cropped area. An approach that harnesses both chemical and biological power is only possible if pesticides are used rationally. With the definition of
55 good farming practice gradually changing, there is every prospect of the integrated approach gaining widespread acceptance in the future.

(a) Use the organisms mentioned in the passage to draw a diagram representing *one* example of a food chain involving a cereal crop. Identify the trophic level of each organism.

(3)

(b) (i) Suggest how the use of insecticides can lead to evolution of resistant populations of the insects that they are meant to kill (lines 12–13).

....

....

.... (3)

(ii) Some of the work described in this passage was sponsored by a chemical company. In view of your answer to part (a) above, what might be the advantage to the company of limiting the use of the insecticide it produces?

....

.... (2)

(c) Why do hoverflies need to consume pollen before they lay eggs (lines 42–43)?

....

.... (2)

(d) Explain *two* different ways in each case in which yield would be reduced by:

(i) aphids feeding on the leaves of cereal plants (lines 7–8);

....

....

....

.... (4)

(ii) flowering weeds growing with the crop (line 49).

....

....

....

.... (4)

(e) Describe *two* ways in which indiscriminate use of herbicides to control weeds could lead to an increase in the number of insect pests in a crop.

....

....

....

.... (2)

(f) The graph shows the change in numbers of aphids and their main predators in an untreated cereal crop.

Describe how you would expect the graph to differ if the crop were sprayed at Time X with a broad-spectrum insecticide.

....

....

.... (3)

2 The diagram represents the energy flow in kJ m⁻² year⁻¹ through the community in one area of sea in the English Channel.

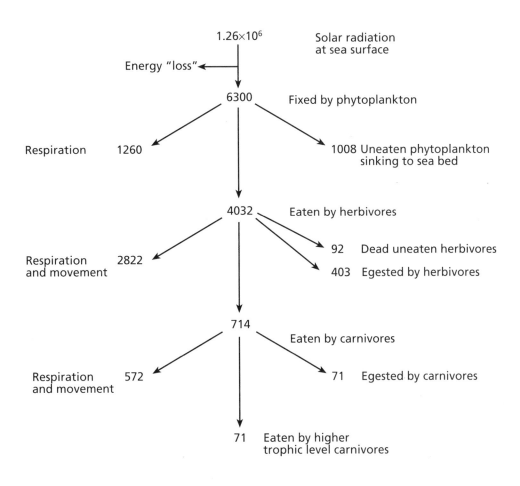

(a) (i) What percentage of the energy at the sea surface is fixed by the phytoplankton?

.... (1)

(ii) Give *two* reasons for the "loss" of energy at this stage.

....

.... (2)

(b) Calculate:

(i) the net primary production;

.... (1)

(ii) the total energy available to decomposers

.... (1)

AEB

3 The diagram shows the energy flow through a fresh-water ecosystem.

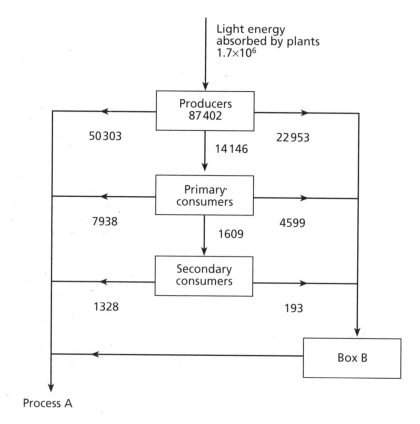

All units are kJ m^{-2} year^{-1}.

(a) Name:

    (i) process **A**;

        .... (1)

    (ii) the group of organisms represented by Box **B**.

        .... (1)

(b) Showing your working in each case, calculate:

    (i) the percentage efficiency with which light energy is converted into energy in producers;

        .... (2)

    (ii) the amount of energy which goes to tertiary consumers.

        ....

        .... (2)

AEB

4 One method of sampling populations in an ecological study is to use a quadrat. A quadrat is an area of known size. Individuals of a population are not distributed uniformly, so if an estimate of density is to be made, a system of *random sampling* must be adopted.

(a) (i) Describe how random sampling can be carried out.

....

.... (2)

(ii) Suggest *one* limitation of random sampling methods.

.... (1)

(b) (i) Describe how you could use a quadrat to estimate the percentage frequency of plants in a habitat.

....

....

.... (3)

(ii) Suggest *one* way in which quadrats could be used to study changes in plant populations.

....

....

.... (3)

(c) Describe *one* method you could use for sampling the animals present in a *named* habitat.

....

.... (2)

ULEAC

5 (a) Explain *one* advantage of improving soil fertility by means of leguminous plants rather than by adding nitrogen-containing fertilisers.

....

.... (2)

QUESTIONS

The table shows the results of an investigation into the effects of different strains of *Rhizobium* and different amounts of nitrogen-containing fertiliser on the growth of a leguminous plant, the ground-nut. The growth is recorded in grams of fresh mass per plant.

Fertiliser added/ kg ha^{-1}	Fresh mass per plant /g		
	No Rhizobium	Strain 411	Strain 1348
0	7.0	12.4	9.7
20	8.4	7.7	7.7
40	9.4	6.6	8.0

(b) (i) Represent the data in the table as a suitable barchart.

(4)

(ii) Summarise the main trends shown by the data.

....

.... (2)

Graph 1

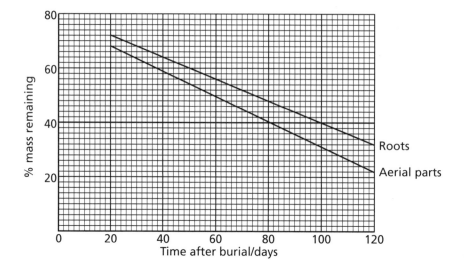

At the end of the growing season, the ground-nut plants were removed from the soil and the aerial parts and the roots were separated from each other. These were then buried separately in the soil and, as they decomposed, the percentage mass remaining was recorded at different times. The results are shown in **Graph 1**.

(c) (i) Calculate the mean rate of decomposition of the roots and of the aerial parts of the ground-nut plants. Show your working.

....

.... (2)

(ii) Suggest an explanation for the difference in the rates of decomposition.

....

.... (2)

(iii) Explain how nitrogen in the ground-nut plants is made available to the next crop.

....

....

....

.... (4)

Graphs 2 and **3** show the results of a separate investigation into the effects of pH on the yield and on the number of root nodules in another two species of leguminous plant.

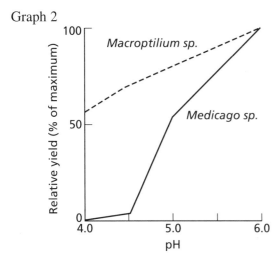

Graph 2

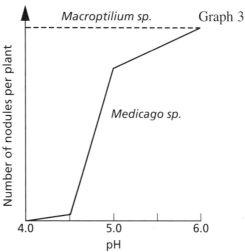

Graph 3

In order to explain the effect of difference in pH on the growth of leguminous plants, it was suggested that poor growth was due to *Rhizobium* being unable to grow in acid soils.

QUESTIONS

(d) Using information in **Graphs 2** and **3**, explain *one* piece of evidence that:

(i) supports this hypothesis;

....

....

(ii) suggests that the hypothesis is not correct.

....

.... (4)

AEB

6 Dieldrin, an organochlorine insecticide related to DDT, was widely used in the UK in the late 1950s as a seed dressing and in sheep dips.

The table below gives some data about the population of peregrine falcons in Great Britain for 1961 and 1975. The populations of these birds of prey were estimated in terms of percentage of suitable territories in which nesting took place (listed as "% territories with young reared"). Note that the highlands of Scotland are mountainous with a cold, wet climate, whereas the Southern Uplands are low hills with fertile soil and a milder climate, more suitable for arable farming. Both the Southern Uplands and Wales are also farmed intensively for sheep. Study the data and answer the questions which follow.

Region	% Territories occupied		% Territories with young reared	
	1961	1975	1961	1975
Scotland				
Western Highlands	86	88	40	62
Central Highlands	92	93	25	43
Southern Uplands	56	69	15	39
England & Wales				
Northern England	52	55	9	23
Southern England	31	62	4	21
Wales	31	71	9	41

(a) Suggest *one* reason why the population of peregrines increased overall between 1961 and 1975.

.... (1)

(b) Suggest *one* effect of toxic levels of dieldrin on peregrine falcons.

.... (1)

(c) Why were there more territories occupied in 1961 in the Western and Central Highlands than in the Southern Uplands?

.... (1)

(d) Suggest *one* reason why there was such a marked increase in the population of peregrines in Wales between 1961 and 1975.

.... (1)

(e) Dieldrin has little effect on the population of wood pigeons, one of the peregrine's most important prey species. Explain concisely why the peregrine is poisoned whereas the wood pigeon is not.

....

....

....

.... (2)

Oxford

7   The Magnox nuclear power station at Berkeley in Gloucestershire was the first in Britain, if not in the world to be decommissioned.

(a) Suggest **three** problems faced by the engineers responsible for decommissioning Berkeley.

1.   ....

....

2.   ....

....

3.   ....

.... (3)

(b) Suggest **two** advantages to the environment of generating electricity from nuclear power.

1.   ....

2.   .... (2)

Oxford

Answers

1 ENERGY AND LIFE

Question			Answer	Mark
1	(a)	1	ATP	**1**
		2	reduced NAD.	**1**
	(b)		carbon dioxide	**1**
	(c)		Your answer should mention three main points:	
			the presence of a chain of electron carriers	
			the chain ends when the electrons pass to oxygen	
			ATP is produced.	**3**

> **Examiner's tip** This is a very common method of assessing your knowledge of a flow diagram involving energy transfer. It often appears in questions relating to respiration or photosynthesis. There are many ways of representing such an energy flow and it would be wise to familiarise yourself with several of these rather than learn just one type. For part (c) you would not gain credit for just saying that 'in the presence of molecular oxygen, much ADP is converted to ATP by phosphorylation'. This is not an *explanation*, which is demanded by the question.

2	(a)	(i)	Productivity rises as more carbon dioxide is available for photosynthesis.	
			At 700 to 900 ppm the rate of increase is less since other factors are limiting productivity.	**2**

(Two of these points would give you <br> maximum marks for this question)

		(ii)	From 900 to 1100 ppm the productivity stays the same carbon dioxide is not limiting *or* another factor becomes limiting.	
			From 1100 to 1300 ppm, the productivity falls *or* productivity steadies then falls, excess carbon dioxide inhibits productivity.	**2**

(Two of these points would give you <br> maximum marks for this question)

	(b)	(i)	1 Maximum increase = 3 units; % increase = 25%	
			2 Maximum increase = 12 units; % increase = 48%	
			3 Maximum increase = 20 units; % increase = 74%	**3**
		(ii)	Increased light intensity increases productivity *or* photosynthesis light provides greater energy input *or* more reducing power for dark reaction.	**2**
	(c)		At high light intensity, carbon dioxide limits productivity *or* photosynthesis because atmospheric concentration of carbon dioxide is low *or* is only 300 ppm.	
			Carbon dioxide is the raw material for photosynthesis.	
			Carbon dioxide provides inorganic carbon for organic compounds.	
			Carbon dioxide combines with ribulose bisphosphate *or* carbon dioxide is reduced	

Question	Answer	Mark

forms carbohydrates *or* named compounds.
Excess carbon dioxide has an inhibitory effect on photosynthesis.   **3**

(Three of these points would give you
maximum marks for this question)

(d)   To eliminate temperature as a variable *or* temperature affects the rate
of carbon dioxide fixation.   (1)

(e)   The rate of the dark reaction is affected by temperature

at low temperatures, increased carbon dioxide may increase the reaction rate

at high temperatures extra carbon dioxide is present from respiration

at low temperatures carbon dioxide may be less soluble *or* harder to absorb

adding carbon dioxide increases the concentration gradient, making carbon
dioxide uptake easier.   (2)

(Two of these points will give you
maximum marks for this question)

Examiner's tip   Note the large number of alternative answers for parts of this question.
This illustrates how an examiner wishes to give you credit for understanding rather
than memorising written text. There is plenty of opportunity for you to express your
understanding in a variety of ways. Note that in part (a) full marks will be gained
only by writing *both* a description and a comment. In part (b)(ii), full credit would not
be given for just saying that increasing light intensity increases productivity. Some
explanation is needed for full credit.

---

3   (a)   The tallest absorption peaks are in the red and blue areas of the spectrum,
much more than in green.   **1**

(b)   Blue   **1**

(c)   Green is reflected *or* not absorbed   **1**

(d)   *a* absorbs more in red than *b*

b absorbs more in blue than *a*

absorption peaks do not coincide *or* are at different wavelengths.   **2**

(e)   Yellow areas contain carotenoids

carotenoids harvest light to pass on to chlorophylls.   **2**

(f)   Measure the percentage light passing through a chlorophyll solution in a
colorimeter.   **1**

(g)   The absorption spectrum is lower than the action spectrum

They follow the same general shape *or* show that the wavelengths most
strongly absorbed also produce the greatest increase in photosynthesis.   **2**

(h)   Light harvesting

protection of chloroplast pigments.   **2**

(i)   Chlorophylls are insoluble in water

Question	Answer	Mark

chlorophylls are membrane-bound molecules

membranes contain lipids and chlorophyll pigments must be separated from the membranes.

2

Examiner's tip Here is an example of a question that requires skill to interpret graphical data, combined with an understanding of the role of chlorophyll in photosynthesis. This type of graph is very common as the basis of data-handling questions and appears in this or in a modified form in most standard textbooks. Note that you are expected to be familiar with the use of a colorimeter for part (f). Note that in part (i) it is not sufficient to say that chlorophyll dissolves in the solvent. To gain full credit you must recognise that the membrane of the chloroplast needs to be broken down by the solvent.

4 (a) Grana *or* thylakoids *or* lamellae *or* quantosomes **1**

(any one)

(b) (i) Photolysis *or* photochemical splitting of water **1**

(ii) Passed to electron carriers

replace electrons lost from photosystem *or* chlorophyll **1**

(iii) Used to reduce NADP. **1**

Examiner's tip This question illustrates the need to understand such flow diagrams rather than learn any particular one. You probably have never seen this actual representation, but if you really understand the process of energy transfer in photosynthesis, then this should not be a problem to you. Note that (b)(i) asks for the name of a process. Therefore, just 'splitting water' would not gain credit.

5 (a) It shows that glucose alone does not affect methylene blue *or* methylene blue does not go colourless on its own *or* it provides a comparison. **1**

(b) (i) Hydrogen *or* electrons

from glucose *or* respiratory intermediate decolorised the methylene blue. **2**

(any one)

(ii) Small amount of suitable hydrogen source in yeast culture

or low level of respiration *or* low hydrogen production. **1**

(any one)

(c) Oxygen from air

accepts hydrogen from reduced methylene blue *or* oxidises methylene blue. **2**

Examiner's tip Familiarity with this experimental procedure would be an advantage in answering a question like this. Even if you haven't used methylene blue in this actual context, i.e. with yeast, you should know the principle of using it as a hydrogen acceptor and you should be able to apply it to any laboratory situation. Note that for part (c), just saying that methylene blue is oxidised would not gain full credit.

Question	Answer	Mark

6 (a) (i) Light

(ii) Keep the temperature constant

(iii) Chlorophyll molecules are saturated with light

or maximum rate of photosynthesis has been reached

or carbon dioxide has become limiting factor.

(iv) Red filter - reduces bubbling; green filter – reduces bubbling to virtually zero.**4**

(b) As there is no carbon dioxide to react with ribulose bisphosphate and change it into glycerate-3-phosphate

ribulose bisphosphate increases and glycerate-3-phosphate decreases.   **2**

Examiner's tip   The question is based on a practical investigation that should be familiar to you. Again, it would be to your advantage if you had carried out this experiment yourself and were aware of the technique involved. Note that for part (b) it is not sufficient to just say that ribulose bisphosphate increases and glycerate-3-phosphate decreases. There must be an attempt at an explanation for full credit to be awarded.

2 THE CELL

Question	Answer	Mark

1 (a) Homogenizing *or* macerating

centrifuging to separate mitochondria.   **2**

(b) Description of an experiment, e.g. using oxidising/reducing agent such as methylene blue, and consequent colour change.   **2**

(c) (i) Crista   **1**

(ii) 0.25 – 1.5 microns   **1**

(iii) A; E; D   **3**

(iv) pyruvic acid *or* pyruvate *or* ADP

ATP   **2**

(v) To combine with *or* remove electrons *or* hydrogen as water *or* act as terminal hydrogen acceptor

and hence allow reoxidising and recycling of hydrogen carriers.   **2**

Examiner's tip   This is a question that requires recall of the structure and function of mitochondria. Note that none of this could be answered by deduction or observation. Note that in (c)(v) an *explanation* is needed for full credit rather than just a statement about oxygen combining with hydrogen.

Question	Answer	Mark
2 (a)	3 axes labelled correctly	**3**
	2 curves correctly plotted and each labelled	**4**
	large scales chosen for presentation	**1**

[Graph: vertical axis left "Potassium ion concentration" (0 to 60), vertical axis right "Rate of sugar consumption" (0 to 40), horizontal axis "Oxygen percentage" (0 to 70). Solid curve with × markers rising steeply then levelling near 50; dashed curve with ○ markers rising to ~38.]

(b) (i) Some potassium ions are always present in the root cell sap

simple diffusion of ions inwards would occur. **2**

(ii) The membrane is taking up potassium actively

this requires energy from respiration and so oxygen is required. **2**

(iii) Maximum amount of potassium ions that can be taken in has been reached

or diffusion outwards may begin to occur
or too much oxygen can begin to act as an inhibitor *or* poison. **2**
(any 2)

(iv) Sugar is being used up for aerobic respiration *or* ATP production, and
this is independent of active transport of potassium ions. **1**

Examiner's tip The skill of translating tabular information into graphical information is being tested. The controlled variable is oxygen percentage and should be on the horizontal axis. The scale for potassium ion concentration should be on the left hand side (vertical axis) and the scale for the rate of sugar consumption on the right. At least half of the grid should be used for the 'large presentation' part of the answer in part (a).

Interpretation of the data by applying your biological knowledge is essential to correctly answer the rest of the question. Note that where *explanations* are required, simple statements or descriptions will not gain full credit.

Question	Answer	Mark

3 (a) (i) A glycerol

B fatty acids *or* hydrocarbon tail of fatty acids.   **2**

(ii) Part A *or* glycerol is more soluble *or* hydrophilic (*or* converse)   **1**

(b) (i) Bimolecular layer with phospholipids correctly arranged   **1**

(ii) Appearance as two dark layers separated by a light one
matches electron-transmitting properties *or* relative size of parts of molecules.
Freeze-fracture will separate layers between fatty acids

Similar appearance on both halves   **2**

Examiner's tip This requires a mixture of recall and understanding and illustrates the considerable depth of detailed knowledge that is required for some answers.

4 (a) (i) A plasma membrane *or* plasmalemma *or* cell membrane

B phagocytic vesicle *or* food vacuole *or* phagosome

C lysosome *or* Golgi vesicle

D Golgi body   **4**

(ii) Label ribosome on rough endoplasmic reticulum   **1**

(iii) RNA synthesis

ribosome assembly   **2**

(iv) Modification *or* glycolysation of products *or* proteins

Cell plate *or* new cell wall formation

Production of secretory vesicles *or* exocytosis *or* lysosome formation *or*
reference to packaging *or* zymogen synthesis.   **1**
(any 1)

(b) (i) Phagocytosis   **1**

(ii) Engulf *or* digest *or* remove foreign organisms *or* bacteria *or*
antigen-antibody complexes *or* dead tissue.   **1**

Examiner's tip Note that there are several alternative answers for part (a) (iv), but part (iv) only has one line for the description. Therefore one sentence would be an adequate answer. All the parts to this require recall. Note that for part (a)(iii), only mentioning one point in the mark scheme would not gain full credit.

5 (a) A cell membrane

B mitochondrion   **2**

(b) (i) Cell surface folded

to give a larger surface area.   **2**

Letts
Q&A

Question	Answer	Mark

(ii) Abundant mitochondria

to provide energy for active uptake | 2

Examiner's tip This topic is very suitable for assessment using electron micrographs and photomicrographs. Recall is required, but observation and the application of biological knowledge are also assessed in part (b). You may not have seen this particular electron micrograph but you will be expected to recognise the features shown, i.e. microvilli and mitochondria. You will also be expected to be able to relate these structures to their functions. You will benefit by having seen as many electron micrographs of cells as possible.

6

Structure	Liver cell	Palisade cell	Bacterium
Nuclear envelope	✓	✓	✗
Cell wall	✗	✓	✓
Microvilli	✓	✗	✗
Chloroplasts	✗	✓	✗

4

Examiner's tip This requires basic recall. One mark will be allocated for each correct horizontal row. Do not guess the answers by filling in all ticks or all crosses.

7 (a) Diagram (spatial relationships correct) | 3
Labels (allow any 6 suitable labels) | 3

Cell inclusion
(e.g. food reserve or pigment)

DNA

Cytoplasm

Slime layer

Cell wall

Cell membrane

Flagellum

Ribosome

(b) No true nucleus *or* no nuclear mebrane
no membrane-bound organelles
no endoplasmic reticulum
no histone proteins in nucleus
no cilia *or* flagella with 9,2 structure
no microtubules
no mitosis
small ribosomes
circular chromosome. | 2

3 LIFE PROCESSES

Question	Answer	Mark

1 (a)

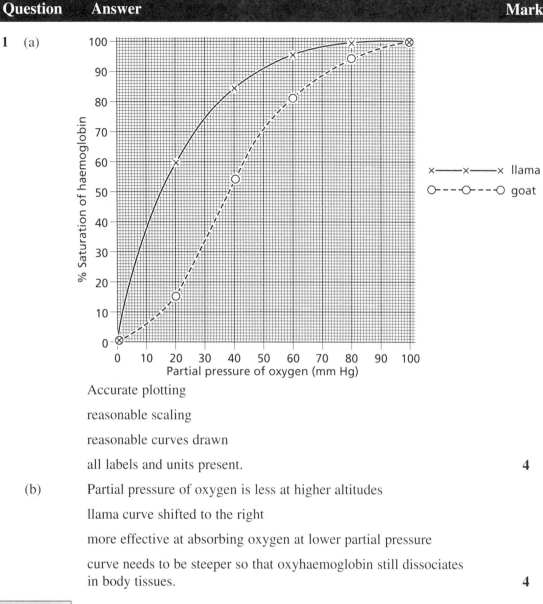

Accurate plotting

reasonable scaling

reasonable curves drawn

all labels and units present. **4**

(b) Partial pressure of oxygen is less at higher altitudes

llama curve shifted to the right

more effective at absorbing oxygen at lower partial pressure

curve needs to be steeper so that oxyhaemoglobin still dissociates in body tissues. **4**

Examiner's tip Note this typical mark scheme for plotting a graph. Use a fine HB pencil for accurate plotting. Make sure your scale uses almost all of the grid provided. Draw the best-fit curve and remember not to extrapolate it beyond the points actually plotted. Accuracy of labelling the axes with complete and correct units is essential. The topic of dissociation curves for haemoglobin often appears as a basis of A-level questions. *Explanations* of such curves are often demanded as answers; just describing the curves would not be enough to gain full credit.

---

2 (a) A Vena cava
B Purkinje fibres **2**

(b) The delay between the atrio-ventricular node and the ventricle allows the atrial contraction to be completed before the ventricular contraction.

The base of the ventricle contracts before the apex of the ventricle, so that blood is forced upwards. **2**

Question	Answer	Mark
(c) (i)	The X should be near the atrio-ventricular node	1
(ii)	This is so that impulses pass down the Purkinje fibres and pass to both ventricles.	2
(d)	There are chemoreceptors in the aortic and carotid bodies	
	impulses pass to the medulla of the brain	
	the impulses pass via the sympathetic system	
	to the sino-atrial node.	4

Examiner's tip Unlike the previous question, which relies almost entirely on deduction and interpretation of data, this requires a great deal of in-depth recall. It illustrates just how much detail is required for many A-level questions and emphasises the need for thorough revision of descriptive topics. Note the completeness of the explanations that would be needed for full credit.

3 (a)	The dye in the blood passes the sample point, goes back to the heart and is soon pumped through the sample point again.	1
(b)	Blood is being pumped at a faster rate.	1
(c)	First peak is at 3 seconds, second peak is at 12 seconds	
	Time = 12 − 3 = 9 seconds.	2
		(1 mark for calculation 1 mark for the answer)
(d) (i)	$70 \times 80 \text{ cm}^3 = 5600 \text{ cm}^3 = 5.6 \text{ dm}^3$.	2
		(1 mark for calculation; 1 mark for answer if the units are correct)
(ii)	$\dfrac{25000}{170} = 147 \text{ cm}^3$.	2
		(1 mark for each part)

Examiner's tip A sound knowledge of blood cirulation is needed to answer this question, together with an understanding of the term stroke volume (the volume of blood pumped at each beat). The mathematics required is very basic, but the numbers that you have to handle will be more quickly dealt with if you have a calculator.

4 (a)	A villus	
	B crypt	
	C smooth muscle	3
(b)	One named part plus a description of its function from any of the following:	
	Villi give large surface area; for absorption of digested food	
	or rich capillary network; for absorption *or* transport of food	

Question	Answer	Mark

or muscle layer; for peristalsis *or* movement of food

or glandular lining; for secretion of enzymes

or lacteals; for fat absorption.   **2**

Examiner's tip This is typical of a 'confidence-building' structure and function question, which involves very basic recall and is often positioned towards the beginning of an A-level examination paper. You will see from the mark scheme that there are several alternative answers to part (b) but, for any one of the alternatives, both the name of the part plus its function will be needed for complete credit.

---

5 (a)   Drawing with protein filaments the same length

thin filaments must be shown to have moved towards each other.   **2**

(b)   Correct position of line, vertically through thick and thin filaments.   **1**

(c)   (i)   Promotes binding of actin and myosin

or formation of cross-bridges.   **1**

(ii)   Energy is needed for cross-bridge cycle

or allows actin to be pulled in.   **1**

Examiner's tip This requires a sound knowledge of the sliding filament theory of muscle action. Questions on this topic often appear and you are advised to thoroughly revise the biochemical details at a molecular level. It would not be sufficient in (c) (ii) just to state that energy is used for contraction.

---

6 (a)   (i)   A nerve fibre and its skeletal muscle fibres.   **1**

(ii)   They are receiving imputs from different motor nerves

or motor fibres are of different lengths.   **1**

(b)   Acetylcholine is released from the end plate and diffuses across the gap

the acetylcholine molecules fit the receptors on the sarcolemma

increasing ion permeability.   **3**

(c)   (i)   Lactate is taken to the liver

oxidised

to produce ATP

some is converted to glucose *or* glycogen.   **3**

(any 3 parts)

(ii)   Stores energy

to maintain levels of ATP

which is rapidly depleted *or* takes a long time to replace.   **2**

(any 2 parts)

Question	Answer	Mark
(d)	They maintain posture for a long time	
	important not to get fatigued.	2
(e) (i)	Few mitochondria	
	limits aerobic pathway.	
	Fewer capillaries	
	so less oxygen supplied.	4
(ii)	Myosin ATPase activity is very high	
	so most ATP will be for muscle contraction.	
	Well-developed sarcoplasmic reticulum	
	means improved calcium supply for muscle contraction to occur.	4

Examiner's tip This is an example of a longer question that requires a great deal of knowledge with understanding. It brings together concepts of nervous control of muscle fibres and the energetics of muscle physiology. Note that to gain full credit for part (e), both an *explanation* and *evidence* will be needed.

4 CO-ORDINATION

Question	Answer	Mark
1 (a)	A lamella	
	contains light-sensitive pigment.	
	B peduncle	
	forms synapse with sensory neuron.	4
(b)	Upward arrow	1
(c)	High acuity *or* low sensitivity *or* colour	2

Examiner's tip Almost invariably, questions on sense organs are mainly concerned with recall of information. This serves to illustrate the depth of treatment necessary to answer a typical A-level question on vision.

2	morning; evening; diurnal *or* circadian; 24; sleep; hypothalamus	6

Examiner's tip All that is required here is recall of information. Be prepared for this type of 'filling in the blank' type of question and the depth of treatment necessary at A level.

3 (a) (i)	A amplifies vibrations *or* transmits vibrations	
	B awareness of position *or* movement of the head/balance.	2

Question	Answer	Mark

(ii)

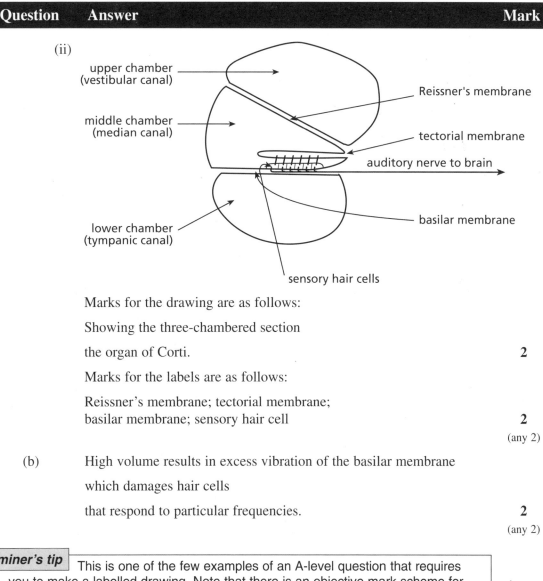

upper chamber
(vestibular canal)

middle chamber
(median canal)

Reissner's membrane

tectorial membrane

auditory nerve to brain

lower chamber
(tympanic canal)

basilar membrane

sensory hair cells

Marks for the drawing are as follows:

Showing the three-chambered section

the organ of Corti.   **2**

Marks for the labels are as follows:

Reissner's membrane; tectorial membrane;
basilar membrane; sensory hair cell   **2**
                                                                (any 2)

(b)   High volume results in excess vibration of the basilar membrane

which damages hair cells

that respond to particular frequencies.   **2**
                                                                (any 2)

Examiner's tip   This is one of the few examples of an A-level question that requires
you to make a labelled drawing. Note that there is an objective mark scheme for
this and you are not awarded marks for inaccurate sketches. Lines should be clear
and made with a sharp HB pencil. Marks are given for accuracy of proportion and
correct detailed labelling. Although most of the marks for this question are for recall,
you can gain an idea of the sectional view required from the diagram given in
part (a).

---

4   (a)   Unequal distribution of ions

more sodium ions outside the neuron than inside.   **2**

(b)   (i)   Sodium ions move in

because threshold level has been reached.   **2**

(ii) Sodium ions are pumped out

potassium ions diffuse out.   **2**

(c)   Potassium ions are diffusing out

preventing the impulse travelling in the wrong direction.   **2**

Question	Answer	Mark
(d)	Increase in the amount of extracellular sodium ions.	2

5 (a) (i)	Both cause elongation *or* growth to be greater than the control GA does not cause much increase *or* causes a little increase IAA causes more than double *or* much greater increase than GA when together, the effect is enhanced *or* greater *or* larger.	4
(ii)	Synergism *or* positive interaction	1
(iii)	They have the greatest effect over the first 24 hours of the experiment. After that time cells have reached maximum size *or* cells are not so responsive to GA/IAA.	2
(b)	As there are several alternative answers to this question any two of the following would gain credit: Mobilises seed reserves *or* promotes better/more uniform germination. Use in brewing *or* malting *or* alcohol production. OR Breaks dormancy in seeds *or* buds. Does away with chilling period *or* earlier crop *or* controlled cropping. OR Promotes flowering in long-day plants *or* inhibits it in short-day plants. Allows growth production of flowers all the year round. OR Promotes seed *or* fruit development. Allows early *or* controlled fruit development *or* seedless fruits. OR Promotes cell division. Use in tissue culture.	4

Question	Answer	Mark
6 (a)	A cerebral hemisphere *or* cerebrum	
	B cerebellum	
	C medulla oblongata	**3**
(b)	A receives sensory information *or* sends out motor information *or* is the association area *or* site of intelligence *or* personality *or* memory	
	B balance *or* co-ordination	
	C reflex activity *or* control of breathing *or* heart rate *or* blood pressure *or* reflexes of swallowing *or* salivation *or* sneezing *or* vomiting *or* coughing	**3**
(c) (i)	No feeling from that area and no movement	**1**
(ii)	No feeling, but movement remains	**1**
(iii)	No movement, but feeling remains	**1**

Examiner's tip   Although the first parts test recall, you will need to understand the basis of a reflex arc to answer part (c).

5 HOMEOSTASIS

Question	Answer	Mark
1 (a) (i)	Organic *or* regulatory *or* active in low concentrations.	**2** (any 2)
(ii)	Plant hormones are only concerned with growth.	
	They do not always act at a distance from their site of production.	**2**
(b) (i)	Y is not identical to X.	
	X may not reach the application site in living plants.	
	X may not exist in the concentration applied.	**3**
(ii)	Look for varieties lacking X and look for dwarfism *or* little stem growth.	
	Concentration of X should be higher during stem growth.	**2**
(c)	Weedkiller	
	For cutting propagation.	**2**

Examiner's tip   This involves a critical analysis of experimental evidence gained from a research project. It requires more than just the comprehension of the passage, because you are expected to have an in-depth knowledge of plant hormones. Note the combination of skills needed i.e. comprehension and recall. Do not ignore the possibility that a question could be set which, at first site, is a comprehension exercise, but also demands recall and application of knowledge.

2 (a)	Active transport requires energy *or* ATP	
	produced by aerobic respiration.	**2**

Question		Answer	Mark
(b)	(i)	**A → B**: loss of water produces an increase in concentration of the tubule contents **B → D**: removal of sodium chloride gives a decrease in concentration.	2
	(ii)	Water moves out of collecting duct by osmosis due to higher solute concentration in medulla established by the loop of Henle.	3
(c)		Long loop of Henle gives greater gradient of concentration in the medulla. Longer collecting duct means that more water may be removed by osmosis.	2
(d)	(i)	Hypothalamus	1
	(ii)	Rise in blood temperature detected by receptors in the hypothalamus leads to stimulation of sweat glands by sympathetic nervous system.	3
(e)		Measures core temperature	1
(f)		Body temperature increases on exposure to high daytime temperature. metabolism leads to increasing body temperature. Body temperature decreases as heat is lost *or* radiated to the environment as it cools.	3
(g)		Able to sweat in response to higher temperature losing latent heat by evaporation.	3

Examiner's tip Here is an example of a question that combines concepts of water regulation and temperature regulation. It illustrates the need to revise the topic of homeostasis as a complete process of regulating the internal environment. Beware of learning only one aspect of the process. Questions may be set that bring together the whole idea of homeostasis. When considering your explanations, it is wise to note the number of marks allocated to each. Almost invariably each mark will require one separate point.

3	(a)	Marks will be allocated for mentioning the following points: Blood is taken from a vein *or* vein is surgically connected to an artery in the arm. Dialysate passes in opposite direction in the machine. Diffusion of urea excess water excess salt take place from blood into the dialysate because of the concentration gradient from the blood to the dialysate.	6

Question	Answer	Mark
(b)	Glucose would diffuse out of the patient's blood and would lead to a shortage of glucose (hypoglycaemia).	1
(c)	It is cheaper in the long term *or* the person is more active *or* reduces need for frequent hospitalization.	2

Examiner's tip This tests whether you are aware of how a kidney machine works. It is an example of a question involving medical technology. Note that the assessment objectives of A-level syllabi state that a certain percentage of the marks should be allocated to technological aspects of biology. This topic is a favourite for inclusion in examination papers. Again, the actual diagram may be unfamiliar to you, but you should understand the principle of the kidney machine so that you can apply it to any given diagram.

4 (a)	Movement of water from a region of high water potential to a region of low water potential	
	through a differentially permeable membrane.	2
(b)	Entry of water into root hairs	
	Movement of water across root cortex.	
	Movement of water across leaf mesophyll	
	and into guard cells	
	maintains turgor.	6

(2 marks for each of these points)

(c) (i)	Water potential = pressure potential + solute potential	
	Water potential = +800 + (–1200) = –400 kPa	2
(ii)	800 kPa	1
(iii)	B to A	1
(iv)	B to A	1
(d) (i)	Xylem	1
(ii)	No end walls	
	no cytoplasm to impede water movement.	2

Examiner's tip The importance of being able to cope with calculations based on water relations in plants is emphasised, but note that theoretical knowledge is also needed. Even a precise definition of osmosis is required and a knowledge of the importance of osmosis in a living plant. A very common error that candidates make is to confuse *solvent* with *solution*, and they write about solutions, cell sap, or liquids passing through selectively permeable membranes. Immediately, the examiner will think that such candidates do not really understand osmosis.

Question		Answer	Mark
5 (a)		Loop of Henle	1
(b)		Forces water to leave the collecting duct by osmosis *or* diffusion down an osmotic gradient *or* increasing salt concentration produces an osmotic *or* concentration gradient.	1
(c)	(ii)	Proximal *or* first convoluted tubule	
		Distal *or* second convoluted tubule.	2
	(ii)	Low sodium concentration increases aldosterone secretion *or* level	
		which increases *or* stimulates sodium reabsorption.	2

> **Examiner's tip** For this question you need to be familiar with the counter-current multiplier theory of kidney function. Note that, to gain full credit for (c)(i), it will not be sufficient to write 'tubule' as an answer. You must be more precise and mention both parts. For the two marks in part (ii), *both* points will be needed.

Question		Answer	Mark
6 (a)	(i)	Secondary response is larger and quicker.	1
	(ii)	Primary: B lymphocytes give rise to plasma cells and memory cells	
		Plasma cells synthesise antibodies.	
		Secondary: Additional action of memory cells boosts response.	3
(b)		Between 20 and 30 days to ensure that antibodies from the first response are still circulating and giving protection.	1

> **Examiner's tip** You should be familiar with antigen–antibody reactions during immune responses. Even though it is unlikely that you have seen the actual graphs depicted in this question, the principles of this type of response should be known so that you can interpret the data by using your knowledge and understanding.

6 REPRODUCTION & DEVELOPMENT

Question		Answer	Mark
1 (a)		Continues to fall	
		from day 8 *or* from a day correctly related to the graph.	2
(b)	(i)	Corpus luteum	1
	(ii)	Placenta	1
(c)	(i)	To maintain the corpus luteum *or* supply of progesterone.	1
	(iii)	Rise in HCG in the blood produces a rise in progesterone.	1

> **Examiner's tip** Almost invariably examiners set questions on reproduction that involve data relating to hormones. You would be well advised to concentrate on revising as many forms of such graphs as you can. Note the two separate points for full credit in part (a).

Question			Answer	Mark
2	(a)	(i)	D and E	**1**
		(ii)	G	**1**
	(b)	(i)	Fruit wall *or* pericarp	**1**
		(ii)	Testa *or* seed coat	**1**
	(c)	(i)	7	**1**
		(ii)	21	**1**

Examiner's tip Some students find the 'double fertilisation' in flowering plants difficult to understand. Questions set at this level are typical of the one included here. Most of it involves recall and the difficult part seems to be understanding how the nucleus of the endosperm becomes triploid.

3	(a)		Capillary	
			Vessel has small diameter when compared to size of red blood cell or vessel has thin wall.	**2**
	(b)	(i)	Flexibility of red blood corpuscles	
			leads to distortion *or* squeezing.	
			Photograph represents sections through the blood cells	
			cut in different planes.	**2**
		(ii)	Electron dense/ electrons are unable to penetrate.	**1**
		(iii)	Red blood cells made largely of one material	
			haemoglobin containing element iron;	
			There are different materials in the nucleus	
			such as protein and DNA *or* chromatin.	**3**
	(c)		Proteins *or* organelles	
			undergo changes during preparation.	**2**
	(d)	(i)	Microvilli	
			give increased surface area for absorption.	
			Short distance between fetal blood and maternal blood	
			allows rapid diffusion of materials.	**4**
		(ii)	The shape of the dissociation curve of fetal haemoglobin is different from that of adult haemoglobin.	
			Fetal haemoglobin is fully saturated *or* greater affinity is at lower oxygen tension than mother's haemoglobin	
			Fetal oxyhaemoglobin unloads at a lower oxygen tension in cells	
			because of the effect of increasing carbon dioxide concentration on its affinity for oxygen *or* the Bohr effect.	**3**

(any 3 points)

Answers to Unit 6

Question	Answer	Mark
(e) (i)	Carbon dioxide urea	1
(ii)	Endocrine *or* hormone production such as progesterone *or* oestrogen *or* gonadotrophin *or* lactogen.	2

> **Examiner's tip** The use of an electron micrograph in this context is an unusual method of assessing knowledge of the structure and function of the placenta. It illustrates that the possible use of such electron micrographs is not confined to cytology and can be applied to any topic in the syllabus. You would be well advised to study and interpret as many types of electron micrograph as possible. Also, this question requires knowledge of the mechanism of oxygen transport in blood. It shows how two topics can be integrated in one question and therefore illustrates the importance of complete revision, rather than leaving out topics for the final examination.

Question	Answer	Mark
4 (a) (i)	High lead concentration is associated with low birth mass. Lead is a metabolic poison. Lead is an enzyme inhibitor. Lead is a non-competitive *or* irreversible inhibitor. High lead concentration depresses growth rate.	3 (Maximum 3 marks)
(ii)	Highest zinc concentration is in the middle range. Zinc levels drop off at top and bottom. Zinc is required as a trace element and is an enzyme activator *or* cofactor. Zinc deficiency reduces growth *or* metabolic rate. High concentrations may be toxic.	3 (maximum 3 marks)
(b)	Ingested *or* inspired absorption occurs across appropriate epithelium and metals are carried in the blood to the placenta.	2 (maximum 2 marks)
(c)	Smoking *or* nicotine alcohol *or* named drug protein deficiency premature birth genetic factor.	3

Question	Answer	Mark

5 (a) (i) Follicle stimulating hormone 1

(ii) There is a sharp decrease in follicular diameter *or* size *or* corpus luteum increases in size. 1

(iii) 21 days 1

(iv) Second follicle will not develop

Corpus luteum continues to develop *or* stays the same size *or* does not get smaller. 2

(b) (i) Blastocyst 1

(ii) Close association with maternal vascular system needed for gas exchange *or* elimination of metabolic wastes. 1

(c) (i) Mother's blood pressure would burst fetal blood vessels or mother's sex hormones might affect fetal gender

or maternal and fetal blood groups may be incompatible

or mother's blood may contain toxins

or for protection against some pathogenic organisms. 2

(d) (i) Chorion and fetus both are derived from the zygote *or* blastocyst. 1

(ii) Chromosomes are visible because cells are actively dividing. 1

6 (a) (i) Folicle stimulating hormone 1

(ii) Leads to development of a follicle

ovary then secretes oestrogen. 2

(b) (i) Day 12 *or* 13 *or* 14. 1

(ii) Immediately following first peak in oestrogen secretion. 1

7 INHERITANCE AND SELECTION

Question	Answer	Mark
1 (a)	Conclusion: Colour blindness is more common in males than in females.	
	Explanation: Recessive gene carried on the X chromosome when condition expressed. The single allele is present in the male *or* it is expressed only when the double recessive is present in the female.	
	Conclusion: Incidence differs widely in different populations.	
	Explanation: Genetic drift *or* reference to small *or* isolated populations *or* reference to differences in selection pressure.	**4**
(b) (i)	Sex linkage	**1**
(ii)	B = allele for normal vision	
	b = allele for colour blindness	

	Male		Female	
Parental phenotype:	Colourblind		Normal carrier	
Parental genotype:	X^bY		X^BX^b	
Gametes:	X^b	Y	X^B	X^b
Offspring genotypes:	X^BX^b	X^bX^b	X^BY	X^bY
Offspring phenotypes:	Normal female	Colourblind female	Normal male	Colourblind male

5

Examiner's tip Part (a) is an exercise in the interpretation of data. So marks for the conclusion could be gained without biological knowledge. The explanation requires the application of biological knowledge of the principles of sex linkage. Part (b) tests the understanding of the principles of sex linkage, although knowledge of terms such as phenotype and genotype is also needed.

Question	Answer	Mark
2 (a) (i)	The vector	**1**
(ii)	Restriction endonuclease	**1**
(b)	Identical to human insulin *or* less chance of side effects.	
	Cheaper than extraction from animal sources.	
	No need to kill animals *or* ethical points.	
	Can be produced in large amounts to satisfy the increasing demand.	**3**

(any 3)

Examiner's tip A sound knowledge of the principles of genetic engineering applied to mass production of insulin is necessary. This is a classic example that illustrates aspects of applied genetics and is a favourite topic in examinations.

Question	Answer	Mark
3 (a) (i)	Parents **Nn** × **nn**	
	Gametes **Nn** n	
	Offspring **Nn** (typical) **nn** (nigra)	3
(ii)	Chi squared = $4^2/10 + (-4)^2/10$	
	$= 16/10 + 16/10$ *or* $1.6 + 1.6$	
	$= 3.2$	3
(iii)	5–10% probability that chance alone gives deviation from expected results.	1
(b)	AaBb gametes	
	aaBb gametes	
	All offspring genotypes	
	All offspring phenotypes *or* stated ratio 5 typical : 3 nigra.	4
(c)	Chi-squared is smaller *or* expect this result more often.	2

Examiner's tip This is a typical example of assessing knowledge of the use of statistics in biology. The formula for the chi-squared test is given. Substitution of the formula using the data given is required and in some examples you would be expected to be familiar with the method of calculating the degree of freedom. It also emphasises the need to take a calculator to the examination.

Question	Answer	Mark
4 (a)	Base *or* named base	1
(b)	Each parent ^{15}N-labelled strand acts as a template	
	for the new ^{14}N-labelled strand.	2
(c)	Upper and middle positions marked.	1

Examiner's tip It will be necessary to understand the principle of replication of DNA and its role in protein synthesis, together with the theory of semi-conservative replication.

Question	Answer	Mark
5 (a)	They are easily kept in the laboratory *or* fast breeding,	1
(b)		

	Phenotype A	**Phenotype B**
Wings	Vv	Vv
Legs	Gg	gg

Question	Answer	Mark
(c)	H = normal blood allele h = haemophilia allele	
(i)	Victoria: $X^H X^h$ Albert: $X^H Y$	1
(ii)	50%	1

Question	Answer	Mark
(d)	Sex linked and determined by a recessive allele.	1
(e)	47 chromosomes instead of 46.	1

Examiner's tip Familiarity with *Drosophila* in laboratory genetics practical work would help with the answer to this question. You should revise details of breeding experiments using this organism. It is probably the most common species to be brought into genetics problems at A level.

Question	Answer	Mark
6 (a)	Arrow to O	1
(b)	The repressor molecule combines with the operator.	1
(c)	Lactose combines with the repressor and inactivates it	
	preventing the switching off of the operator gene.	2
(d)	*E. coli* only produces the enzyme when it is needed and therefore does not expend energy unnecessarily.	1

Examiner's tip The question requires knowledge and understanding of the Jacob-Monod theory of gene control. Check that this is within the requirements of your syllabus. It is a specialised genetics topic that may not be part of the syllabus that you are studying.

8 HUMANS AND THE ENVIRONMENT

Question	Answer	Mark
1 (a)	Cereal plant → aphid → hoverfly *or* ladybird *or* parasitoid wasp *or* ground beetle *or* rove beetle → spider	
	The marks are for three correct organisms in a chain.	1
	Arrows showing energy flow.	1
	Producer, primary and secondary consumer identified as 1st., 2nd. and 3rd. trophic levels.	1
(b) (i)	Resistant and non-resistant insects already present.	
	Use of insecticide selects resistant varieties.	
	The proportion of the resistant form in the population increases through selection.	3
(ii)	It will take longer for the resistant varieties to emerge.	
	This prolongs useful life of the chemical and saves on development costs for new insecticides.	2
		(any 2)
(c)	Pollen contains protein which is needed for formation of eggs.	2

Question		Answer	Mark
(d)	(i)	Fewer nutrients supplied to the developing grain	
		since these are consumed by aphids.	2
		or Leaf damage produces less food by photosynthesis.	
		or Transmission of disease *or* viruses	
		reduces plant growth.	2
	(ii)	Competition for water *or* salts *or* light *or* space.	2 (any 2)
		Weeds attract *or* harbour herbivores *or* disease	
		which affect crop.	2
(e)		Kill *or* destroy tussock-forming plants	
		which harbour insect predators over the winter.	
		or Remove wild flowers that provide pollen *or* nectar source essential for develoment of hoverflies.	2
(f)		Decline in both curves	
		then recovery of aphid population before predators	
		since higher toxicity of insecticide to predators.	3

Examiner's tip This is an extremely long question and would only be set as part of an end-of-course paper in some modular courses. It involves a lot of careful reading and combines the assessment of comprehension with knowledge and understanding of some ecological concepts. Practise answering as many types of such questions as possible. Although this topic lends itself to such questions, they can be used in other contexts. Note that extracts from magazines or newspapers are often used as the basis of these types of question.

Question		Answer	Mark
2 (a)	(i)	0.5%	1
	(ii)	Radiation reflected and not used by phytoplankton *or* wavelength not suitable for photosynthesis.	2
(b)	(i)	6300 – 1260 *or* 5040 kJ m^{-2} year^{-1}	1
	(ii)	1574 *or* 1645 kJ m^{-2} year^{-1}	1

Examiner's tip This is a popular method of assessing your understanding of energy flow through an ecosystem. Most of it requires the ability to handle data by using basic mathematics and a calculator. It is rare that you do not need to use units. Most answers to questions involving calculations require correct units to be used.

Question		Answer	Mark
3 (a)	(i)	Respiration	1
	(ii)	Decomposers *or* saprobionts *or* bacteria *or* fungi *or* micro-organsims	1

Question	Answer	Mark

(b) (i) $\dfrac{87403}{1.7 \times 10^6} \times 100\%$

$= 5\% \ or \ 5.14\%$ **2**

(ii) $1609 - (1328 + 193)$

$88 \ kJ \ m^{-2} \ year^{-1}$ **2**

> **Examiner's tip** This is a similar question to the previous one, but note the different method of representing the flow chart. It emphasises the need to be familiar with as many methods of representing energy flow through ecosystems as possible.

---

4 (a) (i) Define the area being studied *or* give a description of it.

Use a table of random numbers to generate co-ordinates for sampling.   **2**

(ii) It does not take into account clumping of organsims *or* it may miss a species *or* some areas are left unsampled *or* it could sample the same area twice.   **1**

(b) (i) Use random quadrats of the same size.

Record presence or absence of species in each quadrat.

Replicate *or* repeat and record total number of quadrats used.

$Frequency = \dfrac{presence}{number \ of \ quadrats} \times 100\%$ **3** (any 3)

(ii) Carry out a transect

across an area of change

or a stated example of a selected area.

Record the plant species.

or Use a fixed quadrat

over a period of seasonal changes

and record plant species.   **3**

(c) Description of a procedure, eg capture/recapture, sweep nets, dip nets, pitfall traps, kick sampling, quadrats.   **2**

> **Examiner's tip** This is an example of a question that tests knowledge of practical ecological technique. Consequently, you will be at an advantage if you have had experience of practical fieldwork. There is no real substitute for first-hand experience in using standard equipment and procedures yourself.

---

5 (a) Cheaper

Fertiliser can be leached out.   **2**

Question	Answer	Mark

(b) (i)

Rhizobium strain

The marks for the bar chart are allocated as follows:

Axes fully labelled (strain of *Rhizobium* and fresh mass per plant)

Points plotted accurately

Plotted bar chart with strains correctly keyed

Neatness and presentation.　　　　　　　　　　　　　　　　**4**

(ii) If there is no *Rhizobium*, there is a positive correlation between the growth and the amount of fertiliser added

or increased fertiliser gives increased yield.

Decrease in growth with added fertiliser if *Rhizoibium* is present (both strains *or* strain 411).

Difference in response in the two strains.　　　　　　　　　**2**

(any two)

(c) (i) Mean rate of decomposition = $\dfrac{\text{loss in mass}}{\text{time}}$

= 0.4% (loss) per day in roots and 0.46% per day in aerial parts.　**2**

(ii) Roots contain a greater proportion of lignin *or* xylem

which is more resistant to decomposers.

or There is softer tissue in aerial parts

which is readily decomposed by decomposers.　　　　　　　**2**

(iii) Soil bacteria *or* fungi feeding saprobiontically

produce ammonia

which is converted to nitrate;

by nitrifying bacteria.　　　　　　　　　　　　　　　　**4**

Question	Answer	Mark

(d) (i) For *Medicago*

there is a correlation between nodule formation and yield

and nodule formation is dependent on pH.   **3**

(ii) Nodule formation of *Macroptilium* is independent of pH.   **1**

> **Examiner's tip** Note that in a question to which so many marks are allocated, the examiner has more scope for assessing a great variety of skills. A thorough knowledge and understanding of the nitrogen cycle is essential for this, together with the ability to convert tabulated data into a bar chart. Also, part (d) requires you to apply your knowledge so that you can interpret graphical data correctly.

6 (a)   The use of dieldrin was banned in the 1960s.   **1**

  (b)   Infertility *or* thinning of egg shells *or* problems affecting nervous system.   **1**

  (c)   Southern Uplands were more intensively farmed so more dieldrin was in the environment *or* birds less likely to nest in intensively farmed areas.   **1**

  (d)   A change to sheep dips without dieldrin following the ban reduced the amount of the insecticide in the environment.   **1**

  (e)   Dieldrin becomes concentrated in the predators at the top of the food chain.

Seed-eating pigeons only show sublethal levels of dieldrin, but birds of prey accumulate the poison in fatty tissues, where it remains.   **2**

> **Examiner's tip** There are many ways in which examiners can assess the effects of humans on the environment. In this case, the example of an insecticide is used. Note that it does not matter if you have studied this particular example. You should know about the effects of concentrating chemicals through food chains. This can be illustrated with heavy metals, insecticides or polychlorinated biphenyls (PCBs).

7 (a)   High levels of radioactivity encountered during dismantling
Reactor core too radioactive to dismantle
Long half-life of reactor core necessitates long isolation time   **3**

  (b)   No sulphur dioxide *or* no carbon dioxide *or* other greenhouse gases *or* no smoke as from fossil fuel
No depletion of fossil fuels   **2**